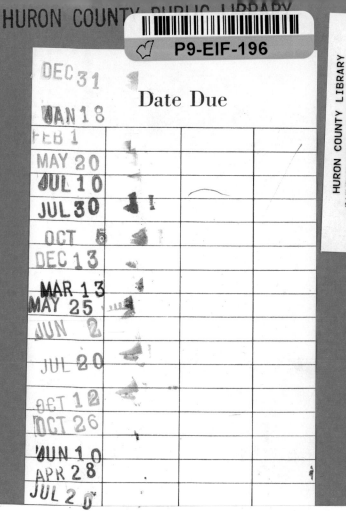

Date Due

DEC 31			
JAN 18			
FEB 1			
MAY 20			
JUL 10			
JUL 30			
OCT 5			
DEC 13			
MAR 13			
MAY 25			
JUN 2			
JUL 20			
OCT 12			
OCT 26			
JUN 10			
APR 28			
JUL 20			

112177

819.8   Needham, Richard John, 1912-
Needh   The hypodermic Needham. Illus. by
        Franklin. Toronto, Macmillan, 1970.
        127 p. illus.

        I. Title.   77862

THE HYPODERMIC NEEDHAM

THE HYPODERMIC
NEEDHAM

by Richard J. Needham

Illustrated by Franklin

MACMILLAN OF CANADA TORONTO

The material in this book first appeared in
The Globe and Mail.

By the same author

Needham's Inferno
The Garden of Needham
A Friend in Needham

*Printed in Canada
for The Macmillan Company of Canada Limited
70 Bond Street, Toronto*

To Earle B. Richards

Contents

HOME AND SCHOOL

NOW SERIOUSLY

TALES OF NOVGOROD

Letter of Introduction

Dear Richard:

Your publishers have asked me to write the introduction to your fourth book, and since I have nothing to gain but fame and fortune, I've agreed to do it. The problem is, I don't really know where to begin.

For instance, should I reveal what you're really like? Many of your teen-age readers will be disillusioned, if not shattered, to discover that you live with your apricot toy poodle in a huge split-level bungalow in Martini Meadows, drive a purple Ferrari with leopard interior, and have your hair styled once a week by Mario of Rome. And they shouldn't be told that although you don't particularly like women, you take one out to lunch at appropriate intervals, effectively protected by your suit of armour and World War I gas mask. After all, you have an image to protect – the Richard J. Needham we adore: impoverished lover of the weaker sex, defender of the young and antagonist of the educational system. Little do your fans know that you play poker nightly with the boys, that you consider anyone under the age of forty irresponsible if not dangerous, and that you yourself have a string of degrees from the University of Bombay, Leningrad Lutheran and Miss Primrose's Finishing School for Girls.

Of course it wouldn't hurt to disclose that you expect me to slave over a hot typewriter four hours a day, two days a week, for a salary that barely keeps me in scallops. And that you limit me to five personal phone calls an hour. And that when we travel, you by DC-8 and I by Greyhound Bus, I end up carrying the infamous gallon bottle of Scotch, your life-sized panda bear and an assortment of suitcases, while you stroll ahead carrying the latest issue of *True Romance* and giving little nods of acknowledgement to your public. Mind you, I'm not complaining. I don't even get flustered any more when you fire 187 instructions at me in a space of three seconds – I've discovered that two chili beans inserted in one's ears effectively block out even the most persistent noise.

And while we're at it, don't you think it's time your readers were told that for all these years it is I who have been writing the column and not you? Certainly they must have guessed by this time that a man simply cannot know that much about women.

But don't worry, Richard. I've decided not to tell the truth. After all, you've been very patient about the times I sleep in until five in the afternoon, and the FM radio, record player and portable colour T.V. I've smuggled into the office. And you didn't even look surprised the time I asked for three months off to recuperate from a severe attack of hangnail. You've been very understanding.

And now I'm going to be equally understanding. I promise not to tell a soul what you're really like, on one or two reasonable conditions.

Firstly, I'm sure you can make your infamous editor, Dietrich Doppelganger, see the necessity of giving me that $200 raise I asked for. After all, it's been three weeks since my last one – I think I've been very patient about it. I'd also be very grateful for an assistant, because I'm tired of getting my own coffee from the cafeteria. As a matter of fact, I'm tired of cafeteria coffee. The only thing it's good for is cleaning my typewriter, and already the 'e' and 'r' keys have become slightly corroded. What I really need in this office is my very own monogrammed espresso machine. It would fit quite neatly between the stereo and the sauna bath.

As for my assistant, what I have in mind is a combination of Paul McCartney, Pierre Elliott Trudeau and Rin Tin Tin. And please make this one human! Last time you tried to pacify me with an adolescent orang-outang. He was a great conversationalist, but he spent too much time swinging from the mobile to be of much help.

The last condition is that you stop showering me with such endearing names as Supertart, Mary Queen of Sots, Thin Lizzie and similar goodies. Your idea of a compliment is to tell someone they're not half as revolting as they look!

I know you'll go along with these few simple requests, because you're such a reasonable and responsible man. Besides, you can't run the risk of losing me. Where else will you find a secretary who knows exactly how cold you like your coffee?

Love and kisses,
Lindy

P.S. I won't be in the office tomorrow or the day after – letter-writing is very exhausting work!

THE HYPODERMIC NEEDHAM

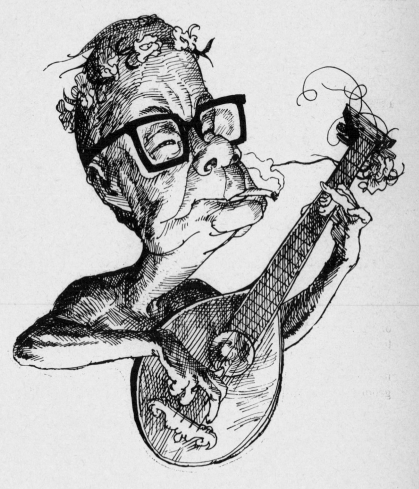

The way some people live

t is truly amazing (said the man at the bar) how people manage to throw away their opportunities, mess up their lives, and make trouble for themselves in 187 different directions.

I know one fellow who by sheer determination and effort became an alcoholic while still at high school, and another who by the time he was 30 owed so much money to the bank that it assigned a team of doctors to make sure he remained alive long enough to pay it back. I know women who were going steady at 14, engaged at 15, married at 16, had a baby at 17, got divorced at 18, remarried at 19, and now are hoping to celebrate their second divorce, their third engagement and their twentieth birthday simultaneously.

For my own part, I have tried to live the quiet, moderate, responsible life characteristic of most Canadians. I went without incident through high school and university, majoring in Groupthink and Jelly Bean Retrieval, which won me a comfortable job with the Dog's Life Insurance Company. Married at the prudent age of 30, I had three children, all of whom got their degrees, and are doing well in their chosen professions.

My wife Esmeralda and I are great friends and do everything together; in fact, we have never been separated one day since our wedding. On Monday evenings we play bridge, on Tuesday evenings it's square dancing, on Wednesday evenings we go to see the human sacrifices at the Maple Leaf Gardens, and so along the line. We spend two weeks in Bermuda every January, coming back with picturesque shells and colour slides to show to our friends. Every other summer, we visit Europe on one of those conducted tours where you see forty-nine cities in twelve days. We always pay cash, have made ample provision for our old age, and possess perhaps the finest collection of Lawrence Welk recordings in Etobicoke.

But those other people! One young chap we heard of was doing well in his law studies when he started sniffing glue; now, he rushes around wearing a lapel button which says, 'Help! The paranoids are after me!' and trying to persuade people that the Jolly Green Giant is in fact a ten foot Pole. A young woman threw up prospects of an excellent marriage and went to Tibet, where she works at a psychiatric clinic treating Abominable Snowmen for their inferiority complex.

Then there's the high school teacher who after twenty years' exemplary conduct entered the classroom one morning, disconnected the speaker system, lit up a cigarette, took a swig from his flask, recited the Lord's Prayer backwards, gave one of the girls a resounding smack on the gluteus maximus, and before being dragged away, announced he had been appointed British Columbia's ambassador to Gabon. There's the woman who after thirty years of apparently happy marriage took her husband down to the used people lot, sold him for $39.52 and went on the bus to Newfoundland, where she convulses the natives with jokes about the gullibility and ignorance of Torontonians.

It's incredible, my dear sir, how some people live – the married couple who haven't spoken to each other for five years but in that time have produced three children: the neighbour who comes home every night so drunk that his wife meets him at the bus stop with a wheelbarrow; the woman who told me at a dinner party, 'I'll have to get rid of my lover; he keeps making snide remarks about my darling husband'; the young man who quit third-year medicine so he could play the garbage-can lid with a folk group called the Neurotic Camshaft, whose specialty is to conclude a concert by hurling fire bombs into the audience.

There's one man who has held eighty-four jobs in his lifetime, quitting thirty-two of them and being fired from the rest; now he's on welfare, and on pleasant summer mornings stands outside the Eglinton subway station, jeering at the taxpayers as they go to work. I heard of another with a regular job but no home; he has four good-natured girl friends and lives with each of them for a week in rotation. With the money thus saved on food and shelter, he hopes to take a fifth girl to Mexico.

A feckless, irresponsible lot, if you ask me. But perhaps you had better not ask me, for I see two sturdy police officers coming through the door and heading in my direction. I wonder what they want me for – that bank job in Hamilton, the LSD find in Montreal, the Winnipeg widow I took for $25,000? No, I think I know what it is; and I will give you, sir, one parting word of advice. If you must murder your wife, don't do it with a hacksaw; it's hard work, and has truly distressing effects on the broadloom.

A prophet is not without profit

Human beings (said the man at the baron the fifty-fourth floor of the Toronto-Dominion Centre) have always been curious; and especially curious about the future. I give you by way of proof the continued popularity of palmists, clairvoyants, astrologists, necromancers, race-track tipsters, and economists.

This business of prophecy has always appealed to me, and I saw a chance of going into it while dining at a Chinese restaurant named the Wun Long Yock. The next table was occupied by a group of career girls, who expressed anger and contempt at the vacuous nature of the fortunes coming out of their cookies – 'Happiness will be found in helping others' – 'Beware of a false friend' – 'Think carefully before acting hastily' – 'Monday is the root of all evil' – and similar garbage.

I spoke to the proprietor about this, suggesting I compose some fortunes with a bit more zap to them, and he consented. Accordingly, the customers got slips of paper saying, 'An interesting and wealthy bachelor will telephone you next Saturday night with a scandalously improper suggestion leading to a trouble-ring ceremony at St. Bingo's', or, 'You'll learn next week that your drinking uncle has died in Volvograd, N.S., leaving you his liverwurst plantation'; or, 'Husband along you fly big bird bimeby; him wing fall off, him go bang; husband along you him kaput.'

Such prophecies brought the restaurant an upsurge of business, but when they failed to materialize, the customers became hostile. The owner was beaten up by a career girl who had sat by the telephone all Saturday night waiting for it to ring; and one of his windows was smashed by a married woman who had blown $200 on a see-through lace jumpsuit to wear at her husband's funeral. From this experience, I learned that some of my predictions, at least, would have to come true.

Setting up for myself as a consultant prophet ($10 for tarot cards, $15 for messing around with tea leaves) I played it more safely – 'You'll get into serious trouble through your total inability to live within your income' – 'You will spend all next week wondering why your life has been such a cruddy failure' – 'As a result of the Trudeau Government's determined fight against inflation, you'll pay 5 per cent more for everything starting tomorrow' – 'Your teen-age son will ask your opinion on something, then spend five hours proving it is wrong, foolish, inconsistent, bigoted, and went out with Wayne King the Waltz King.'

I composed one fortune which read, 'You are going to have a big row with your boy friend over his infidelity.' The girl who opened it immediately telephoned him saying, 'All right, who is she? Where have you been hiding her, you rotten two-timing bastard?', which naturally produced a blazing quarrel between them. I composed a fortune which read, 'Your wife will be in a bad mood when you get home; better have a few drinks to fortify yourself.' The man who opened it had a few drinks, and when he crawled up the front steps some hours later, found his wife ready to have at him with the electric carver.

Winning some reputation for the accuracy of my forecasts, I decided to make real money out of them. Accordingly, I would purchase some cheap mining stock like Congame Expl, predict a sharp rise for it, and sell at a handsome profit as my clients rushed to buy it. Or again I would purchase some acres of bush in North Aorta Township, prophesy that a vast industrial development was going in there, then unload it on the suckers.

Flushed with success, I went for the biggest prize of all, prophesying that the waters of Lake Ontario were about to rise up and engulf

Toronto. As people fled the city for higher ground, I was able to pick up their properties for a song, and now I own something like two-thirds of it. But things haven't worked out precisely as I had calculated. The flood, as you will perceive, has now gone well past the fifty-third floor. Perhaps, after all, there is a God, and perhaps one's sins do find one – aargh, bubble, bubble.

Cyrano de Burlington

nce upon a time there was a country so up-to-date that it had five mail deliveries a week, and that letters had been known to travel from Toronto to Montreal in less than four days. In this country, there was a province where God mainly concerned Himself with bottles, bosoms and bets.

In this province there was a borough named Burlington, so vast in its extent that in the west end people wore ten-gallon Stetsons, in the east end they worshipped a divinity named Joey, and in the north end you could find numerous igloos, around which Eskimos chased polar bears and museum curators chased Eskimos. In this borough there lived a beautiful girl named Roxane Roggenbrot.

There were many young men who admired Roxane, but two who admired her especially, Cyrano and Christian. Christian was brave and handsome, but withal on the simple side. He attended a nearby university called McMonster, where he was in third-year Honours English but found himself handicapped by the fact he could neither read nor write.

Cyrano, too, was brave, but you could scarcely call him handsome, on account of his extraordinary nose – which, if you looked at it from one angle, resembled a cucumber; and from another, a pretzel; and from another, The Archer; and from another, St. Basil's Cathedral in Moscow; and from another the intersection of Highway 27 and the Q.E.W.

People would say to Cyrano, 'No woman could love a man as ugly as you. Why don't you go to a plastic surgeon and get yourself a nose job?' To which he proudly replied, 'It may be a remarkable kind of nose, but it's *my* nose; that's the kind of nose God meant me to have. I would neither affront Him nor demean myself by having it changed, even if that caused half the women in Burlington to fall in love with me.''

Recognizing that Roxane could never love him, Cyrano worshipped her from afar, composing romantic poems about her which he burned afterwards, and writing steamy letters to her which he never mailed. One day, he was sitting by himself at a coffee counter when Christian came in and sat next to him. They got into a lively discussion about love, in the course of which Christian remarked, 'I got this here problem, like. There's this dame, she's really stacked, but I can't get nowhere with her.'

Cyrano said, 'The way to a woman's heart is by writing love letters – long, passionate letters telling her she is the sun, the moon and the stars all rolled into one; telling her she is the most important event since Julius Caesar crossed the Rubaiyat; telling her she has complete, exclusive and perpetual possession of your heart.' Christian said, looking morose, 'But I can't read or write.' The gallant Cyrano said, 'Well, in that case I will write them for you.'

'How much will you charge?' asked Christian, to which Cyrano replied, 'Nothing at all. I'd be very happy to think my love letters were being read by a beautiful woman, even though they advanced the cause of another man. Oh, by the way, women are very impressed if a man brings them flowers.'

Once again, Christian looked morose. 'I can't walk down the street carrying flowers; the guys would think I was a flit or some damn thing. I'd even feel foolish going into a store and buying them.' Cyrano said, 'In that case I will buy the flowers and attach a nice little note signed by you, and take them to her house and put them on the doorstep and then scuttle away. Now all I need to know is this girl's name.'

Christian said, 'Her name is Roxane,' at which Cyrano started so violently that the reverberations were felt at Aldershot C.I., causing half the boy students to awaken from dreams of pushing their fathers over the edge of the Hamilton Mountain, and half the girls to awaken from dreams of seducing Dustin Hoffman, with their mothers being strapped to a chair and forced to watch. Cyrano soon recovered, however, and the deal was made.

Since Cyrano adored Roxane, he settled down with great joy to write her love letters, even though they led her into the arms of another. He started in a small way, with a little jingle which went, 'Moses is dead, Violet sniffs glue, butter loves bread, and I love you.'

Christian reported to Cyrano that this message had been well received, so Cyrano cooked up something more romantic, 'How do I love you? There are big and small ways, and middle-sized; thus I adore you all ways.' Christian reported, 'She told me that when she got it in the mail, she cried so hard with sheer joy that she had to wear dark glasses for the rest of the day.'

Cyrano said, 'I wonder if they should go through the mail? That ordinarily takes eight or nine days, and perhaps a letter might be a bit outdated by the time she gets it. From here on, Christian, I will deliver them myself by dead of night. Every morning, she will find on her front doorstep a bottle of milk, a copy of the *Mop and Pail*, a love letter and a bunch of flowers.'

After this, Cyrano went into high gear. Over Christian's name he wrote letters to Roxane saying, 'Who knows your smile has known a perfect thing,' saying, 'I never look at you, but there is some new virtue born in me, some new courage,' saying 'Take my heart, I shall have it all the more; plucking the flowers, we keep the plant in bloom.'

He wrote, 'Only believe that unto you my whole heart gives one cry; and writing, writes down more than you receive; sending you kisses through my fingertips – lady, O read my letter with your lips.' He wrote, 'Love, I love beyond breath, beyond reason, beyond love's own power of loving! Your name is like a golden bell hung in my heart; and when I think of you, I tremble, and the bell swings and rings – Roxane!'

Running into Christian at this point, Cyrano asked, 'How's it going?' Christian answered, 'Terrific! I have won her heart completely. She follows me to my classroom at McMonster every day and sits at the next desk, gazing at me and sighing and touching my hand and rushing out to buy me cigarettes or coffee whenever I give her the signal. Just a few more letters, Cyrano, and I think she and I will be making beautiful music together.'

Cyrano felt his heart crack, but said nothing, and wrote love letters to Roxane which scorched the paper. Thus it went until in one letter to the girl, he quoted a famous line without identifying the author, 'For thy sweet love remember'd such wealth brings that then I scorn to change my state with kings.' The next time Roxane saw Christian, she said, 'That was a lovely line you quoted in your last letter – the one about scorning to change your state with kings. But you didn't say where it was from, do tell me, I'd like to read some of his stuff.' Christian looked stricken. 'Uh, er, that is, I think it was Spiro Agnew, I mean Ross Thatcher, or perhaps it was Cassius Clay, uh, er.'

Roxane's eyes narrowed. 'Dear Christian,' she said, 'I appreciate your letters so much that I'd like to have you write me one here and now – this moment, in front of me. There's a table with paper and pens; just write me a nice little letter while I watch.' Christian blushed as red as a Toronto subway coach. 'Roxane, I must confess; I cannot read or write; the letters were written by someone else.' Roxane said, 'You must tell me his name, otherwise I will reveal to the McMonster authorities that you are illiterate and you will never attain your ambition of teaching English at a university or community college.'

Christian said, 'His name is Cyrano, and if you'll spare me, I will produce him for you immediately,' which he did. Cyrano informed Roxane, 'I love you but I realize you can never love me on account of my freak beak.' She answered, 'Women don't fall in love with men's noses or ears and anklebones; they fall in love with men. I can tell from your letters that you are a real man, and if this creep Christian would buzz off, we could do something about it,' following which she kissed him tenderly on the end of his proboscis.

Yes, they were married and produced five children, all of whom have inherited not only their father's nose but also his pride and courage. They have fought and beaten every kid at the public school they attend, and can hardly wait for the day when a teacher will come out with some nosy remark. Pow!

The weigh of all flesh

nce upon a time there was a city named Toronto, which (more by accident than by design) had become the wickedest in the world; and in it there was a suburb named Deadlock Dell; and in it there was an apartment house named Bedside Manor; and in this lived a young lady named Ava Dupois.

Ava was good, intelligent, warm-hearted and weighed 175 pounds. You might say that she had a lot going for her. Or you might say that even when fully clad, she left much to be desired. Or you might say that she was generously endowed in all the wrong places. Or you might say, as our grandfathers would have, that she was beef to the heels. But whatever you might say, she still weighed 175 pounds, and sometimes 180.

It need hardly be said that the men of Toronto paid little attention to Ava. Occasionally, as she walked along the street, one man would remark to another, 'It's bad enough seeing a man dressed up as a woman, and still worse seeing a woman dressed up as a woman, but when you run into a hippopotamus dressed up as a woman, you know that the Day of Judgment is at hand. Let's go dancing at the Electric Sarcophagus tonight, Walter.'

Hearing such remarks, Ava shrivelled inside as much as she would have liked to shrivel outside. She thought, 'That does it. Starting tomorrow – well, at any rate starting next week – I am going on the famous 21-day banana diet, in which you throw away the bananas and eat the skins. If that doesn't work, I will try out that new Hollywood diet – air, water, raw carrots and an occasional fish-head. Or I will go to the steam bath and remain there until they have to take me away in a bottle.'

But alas, Ava lacked the will power to do any of these things. One day, after clocking in at 179, she wandered down to the Riverdale Zoo and started crying, when to her surprise one of the apes said to her, 'What's all this blubbering about? Can I do anything to help?' Ava was astonished. 'Are you an ape, or a human, or what?'

The simian replied, 'I am your Hairy Godmother. At one time, they had me in a room of infinite size, where an infinite number of apes were banging away on an infinite number of typewriters. On my first go, I wrote the entire text of the *Encyclopaedia Britannica*; on my second, *Valley of the Dolls*; on my third, the Air Canada domestic schedule. On my fourth try, I slipped a piece of paper into the machine, and typed on it 'The medium is the message', after which they deported me here to the Riverdale Zoo. You are allowed one wish from me, so get cracking, baby, spit it out.'

Ava shot back immediately, 'I want to be lean and slinky, like a fashion model,' at which she felt all her clothes sliding off her. Racing home to the mirror, Ava saw her wish had been granted. She was eight feet tall, with a pale-green complexion, knobby knees, long, stringy hair, hands as long as her forearms, feet as long as her hands, and up top, a couple of fried eggs.

Ava the skinny made even less impression on men than Ava the plump. They took one look at this spooky creature, then leaped five feet into the air, and started speaking with tongues, and raced into the nearest bar. So she went back to Riverdale Zoo, and had another chat with her Hairy Godmother, who tartly observed, 'You had one wish, and I granted it; why the hell should you have a second?' Ava let out a wail so piercing that half the construction workers in Oshawa dropped their tools, and the ape relented, giving her one more wish.

For this wish, Ava had planned carefully. 'I want to be 5 foot 7, weighing 120 pounds, 36 inches upstairs, 34 downstairs, and 23 on the mezzanine, the whole being capped with honey-blonde hair, green eyes, a small turned-up nose, a dimple on the left cheek, and enough sex appeal to sink a Brazilian battleship.' Her Hairy Godmother nodded, and Ava rushed home to behold, in her mirror, the second most gorgeous creature in all Toronto. (Note to any woman stupid enough to ask me, 'You, of course.')

Ava thought to herself, 'At long last, I've got it made. Now to wreck four homes, seven offices, and fourteen investment portfolios,' and she sashayed downtown to post herself at the corner of King and Bay. There she stood for several hours, but no man paid any attention to her at all, unless you include the one who on seeing her, told his male companion, "Doesn't that kind of thing disgust you? Right out in broad daylight, too. Why doesn't someone arrest it or kill it? Cuthbert, dearest, remind me to vote for dear old Allan and Bill in the civic election.'

At this point, we must leave Ava Dupois. What happened to her after that, I don't know, but I hear variously that she stays home every night with the blinds drawn, reading Edgar Benson's *White Paper on Tax Reform;* that she went to Central Africa, where a welcoming committee greeted her with knives, forks, and serviettes; and that she took refuge in Italy, where she's immensely popular with the men, but sometimes looks a bit pinched.

A tale of two cities

I t was the best of times; it was the worst of times; it was the age of wisdom, it was the age of foolishness; it was the spring of hope, it was the winter of despair. It was the time when the French-Canadian separatists had seized power in Montreal, and were giving the works to the English-Canadians. 'Nous serons nous-mêmes, nous serons nous-mêmes, nous serons nous-mêmes toujours!'

The French-Canadians (hereinafter known as the French) imprisoned the English-Canadians (hereinafter known as the English) in such places as the Bonsecours Market, the Rue Berri bus terminal, the Henri-Bourassa Métro station, and a building at Terre des Hommes which they renamed Babbittat.

They charged the English with such heinous crimes as living in Westmount, toasting the Queen, making fun of General de Gaulle's nose, driving at less than 45 m.p.h. on St. Catherine Street, stopping to let pedestrians get safely across, paying their income tax to Ottawa in full and on time, referring to Rue St -Jacques as St. James Street, allowing their women to wear girdles, refusing to take part in the Friday-night folk-dancing sessions at the Place Ville Marie, and believing there actually was such a person as Pierre Elliott Trudeau.

Those found guilty were subjected to such cruel punishments as having to read the editorials in the Montreal *Gazette,* having to ride the entire length of the Métro on a 95-degree afternoon, having to learn French irregular verbs, having to spend a whole day in the Korean Pavilion at Terre des Hommes, and having to listen to a five-hour recorded diatribe by Pierre Bourgault against the English and all their works.

The ultimate penalty, reserved for those English who had really ground the faces of the French, was of course death; to stand upon the scaffold, utter the last words, pray for God's mercy, and swallow the lethal draught – Air Canada coffee in a transparent plastic cup.

Most of the English were permitted to get away with what belongings they could carry, and naturally fled to Toronto, where they arrived by train, bus, plane and private car with their cricket bats, their umbrellas, their field hockey sticks, their woollen tea-cosies, their Wedgwood china, their grandfather clocks, their bound volumes of *Punch,* and their framed photographs of the Royal Family all in bed together.

Getting off at the Union Station, one said, 'My, it's good to be in a city which is British to the corpse, and where you don't have people all around you jabbering in a foreign language.' Another said, 'God save the Queen. First of all I'm going to the City Hall to shake hands with Mayor Tommy Church, and then I will visit Queen's Park for tea and crumpets with Premier George Drew.' Another declared, 'None of this would ever have happened if Paul Martin had still been alive.'

Accustomed to mass arrivals of refugees from yon and hither, Toronto took the whole business in its stride, merely upping apartment rents by 100 per cent, and laying in enormous stocks of Peek, Scream biscuits and peppermint bullseyes. But there was one young woman, Lucy Doornail, in old T.O. who was greatly upset by the coup d'état. Her beloved husband, Charles Doornail, had gone to Montreal on a harmless business trip and had been seized by the French and charged with the capital offence of espionage.

Not knowing how to bring about her husband's release, Lucy wandered into a Bay Street bar, and almost fainted when she saw him sitting there, throwing back Manhattans as fast as the bartender could make them. As she rushed toward him, however, she saw that it wasn't her husband; just a stranger who looked very much like him, who might almost indeed have been his twin brother.

Lucy sat down at the bar and ordered a double brandy, and thought to herself, 'Oh, my poor Charles! He isn't getting any double brandies in that awful Montreal prison; he is probably thankful for a cup of cold water,' and she started weeping so hard that her tears bounced off the counter and into Mr. Look-Alike's Manhattans.

After a while, he turned to her, saying, 'I do not wish to be unpleasant or anything, but I must point out to you that your tears are diluting my Manhattans and extinguishing my cigarettes and bouncing off the bar onto my John Bulloch sports jacket. What's the trouble?'

Lucy Doornail replied: 'It's my poor husband, Charles. He is with the T.T.C. here in Toronto, and he went to look at a new invention that's been introduced on the Montreal subway. They are called escalators, and they move up and down carrying people. Charles thought he might order some for the Toronto subway, instead of which he has been arrested for spying. The penalty is a terrible death – having to mount the scaffold in front of those screaming old bags with their knitting, and drink Air Canada coffee from a plastic container.'

She started crying wildly again. 'Oh, my darling Charles! He likes to have me scrub his back in the bathtub, and he snores with funny whistling noises, and he warms his poor, cold little feet on my bottom, and sometimes he gets up in the middle of the night to eat sardines out of the tin. He's terribly grouchy in the morning until he has his second cup of coffee, and then he says he's sorry and kisses me. He brings me flowers twice a week and once a month he takes me out to a gorgeous dinner at La Scala. Who is looking after him now, and seeing he takes his vitamin tablets, and has a clean shirt every day, and doesn't fall asleep with a cigarette in his hand and set fire to himself? Why do you add to my torment by looking so much like him?' and she hit the unfortunate man over the head with her handbag, causing him to choke on his seventeenth Manhattan.

Restraining her, he said, 'You really do love your husband, don't you? Most of the women who come into this bar would like nothing better than to have their husbands publicly executed; they'd sit right in the front row and cheer. I do wish there were some way I could help

16

you get him out of that Montreal prison and back to dear old T.O.'
Lucy said, 'You could help me by telling me who you are and why you
drink so much,' to which he replied:

'My name is Sydney Cardboard, and drinking is my full-time career
– Bloody Marys in the morning, Manhattans in the afternoon, and
straight Scotch at night.' Lucy asked, 'How do you get the money to
support such a life?' Sydney replied, 'I am subsidized by the W.C.T.U.,
which produces me at its meetings as a horrible example of how liquor
can ruin a man. I really am ruined, too, and expect to perish at any
moment from acute alcoholism. I will go straight to Hell, of course,
where my punishment will be to sit for all eternity at a bar with
hundreds of bottles in front of me, every one of them empty.'

Feeling vaguely sorry for Sydney Cardboard, Lucy said, 'I don't
know about your religion, but according to mine, you do not have to
end up in Hell however wicked your life may have been. You can still
be saved by some noble deed that will send you straight to Heaven,
where Canadian Club comes out of the taps.' Sydney thought about this
as he drained his twenty-third Manhattan. 'Hit me again,' he told the
bartender, and then he turned to Lucy saying, 'I have a wonderful idea;
since I look so much like your husband, why don't I get on the Rapido
and go to Montreal and take his place in the prison?'

Lucy said, 'But how will you get in?' 'That's easy,' Sydney replied.
'They're having a liquor strike in Quebec. I'll take a case of Gilbey's gin
and bribe my way through.' Lucy put her arms around Sydney and then
she planted a great weepy kiss on him, crying, 'This is a far, far better
thing you do than you have ever done.'

Lucy and Sydney went to the Wellington Street liquor store, where
he purchased a case of Gilbey's gin, and then she saw him off to
Montreal on the Rapido. Sydney naturally gravitated straight to the bar,
where he put back one drink after another, occasionally crying, 'This is
a far, far better thing I do than I have ever done,' or 'This is a far, far
better rest I go to than I have ever known,' and at one point asking the
waiter, 'Why are the windows of this bar all blacked out?', to which the
waiter replied, 'The law of Ontario requires it. It is to protect the
decent, godly people who sit in the bar of the Rapido from looking out
and seeing the scandalous alcoholic orgies which take place in the streets
of Belleville, Brockville, Bowmanville, Shannonville and Port Mope.'

Arriving in Montreal, Sydney Cardboard took himself and his case of
Gilbey's gin straight to the place where Charles Doornail was impris-

oned, and had no difficulty bribing the guards to let him into Doornail's cell. They exchanged clothes and documentation, and in little more time than it takes to tell, Doornail walked out of the prison, boarded a plane, and returned to his wife in Toronto.

That evening, a prison guard came to Sydney Cardboard saying, 'You are Charles Doornail, and you have been found guilty of espionage. Tomorrow morning we will tumble you into the tumbril and take you to the scaffold, where you will meet your doom to the massed execrations of Thérèse Defarge and the Sweater Girls. We've arranged a hearty breakfast, and is there anything else you would like?'

Sydney said, 'Yes, I would like to have a woman in my cell overnight.' The guard looked amused, saying, 'Some of you crummy English are almost normal. Any particular woman?' Sydney said, 'Yes, I want the celebrated fille de joie, de tristesse, et d'ivresse, Solange Surputain.' Within an hour or so, Solange arrived; and how do you suppose she and Sydney spent the night? Ah, gentle reader, things are not always – in fact, are hardly ever – what they seem.

When Sydney went to the scaffold the next morning, he had an air of utter serenity, which he retained even when Thérèse Defarge shrieked her foulest maledictions at him. He blew her a kiss, faced the screaming crowd of women, and said in flawless French, 'Mesdames et messieurs: Ça me fait un grand plaisir de me trouver devant une auditoire si intéressante et si enthousiaste. Je me rends compte que je vais mourir, mais je voudrais mieux perir parmi les Montréalais que fleurir parmi les Torontois. Permettez-moi, avant d'avaler la boisson fatale, d'exprimer aussi bien que je peux mon admiration pour la belle civilisation française.'

Sydney proceeded from there to enact a whole scene from Molière's *Le Malade Imaginaire*, taking all the parts; another from Rostand's *Cyrano de Bergerac*; and another from Corneille's *Le Cid*. He recited yards of verse from Victor Hugo, Paul Verlaine, Alfred de Vigny, Alfred de Musset, and Alphonse Lamartine. 'Quand la feuille des bois tombe dans la prairie –'

The knitting women ceased to curse; indeed, several of them laid down their needles and began to applaud; and finally Thérèse Defarge arose to proclaim, 'Cet homme est vraiment du premier rang; je crois qu'il est Québecois; laissez-le vivre!' Everybody cheered, and Sydney stepped down from the scaffold, to be embraced in turn by Mme Defarge and Mlle Surputain.

A happy ending, wouldn't you say? But of course you are wondering how Sydney resolved his triangular problem. He simply rented an apartment on Rue de la Montagne and set up housekeeping with both of them, thus proving what is known to every woman in Montreal, in Toronto, or any place else – that a first-class man can be (and almost invariably is) divided into any number of parts.

A knight there was

nce upon a time, and in Vancouver of all places, there was a very chivalrous young man named Lancelot Lochinvar. He was the modern equivalent of a knight, and if he rode a Honda instead of a horse and wore shiny serge instead of shining armour, he still carried on the knightly tradition.

Lancelot would say, 'My strength is as the strength of ten, because my heart is pure,' and then he would tear the Vancouver telephone book in half with his bare hands, a feat which made him very popular at cocktail parties, and very unpopular with the B.C. Telephone Company. He was always lighting cigarettes for women, and throwing his coat down on puddles for them to walk over, and bringing them flowers which he had lifted from somebody's garden.

One bright morning, Lancelot decided, 'I will spend today going to the rescue of maidens in distress.' But how to find them? He said to one young lady on Howe Street, 'Are you a maiden in distress?' She replied, 'I am in distress all right; I have the father and mother of all hangovers. But unfortunately, I am not a maiden; you might call me a near miss.'

Another young lady said, 'I am a maiden, all right, but I am not in distress; so buzz off, get lost, blow, or I will fire my tear-gas gun into your ugly mug.' A third said, 'I am a maiden and I am in distress. The distress I am in is that of being a maiden, and I trust you will rescue me from it right here and now.' And how did Lancelot respond to this? Why, the way any true knight would. But these three, as he found to his relief, were the exceptions.

Speaking to dozens of maidens (and to thousands of non-maidens), Lancelot learned that most of them were in distress; and in the same kind of distress. They kept putting on weight when they wanted to take it off. One said to him, 'I manage to knock off seven pounds, and then I get this awful empty feeling inside me and then I rush over to Robsonstrasse, and purchase all manner of kirschtorte and apfelstrudel and put eight pounds on again. There is no God.' Another said, 'I don't know why I keep on gaining. It is true I enjoy spaghetti and pizza and hot fudge sundaes, but I always take my coffee black, with saccharine.'

Lancelot couldn't figure out an answer to this, so he went and sat on a bench in Stanley Park. Suddenly, he heard a horrible squealing noise from a clump of trees and went to investigate, and found a poor little dragon lashed to one of them. The beast told him, 'We unfortunate dragons are being terrorized by a fire-breathing princess named Georgia Granville. Please untie me before she comes and turns me into a dragonburger.'

Lancelot did so, at which the dragon said, 'You may now have your reward. It is a magic potion which causes women to lose ten pounds a week regardless of how much pizza or macaroni or chocolate cream pie they may eat. I imagine you could sell it for as much as 25 cents a bottle,' at which Lancelot thought, 'Ha! Little does he know about women! I will sell it for $100 a bottle and become rich beyond the dreams of Avis.' Then the dragon said, 'There is just one difficulty. A woman losing ten pounds every week will have to buy a complete new wardrobe every week, and that might be kind of a nuisance,' at which Lancelot cackled inwardly but politely said, 'Oh, I think the average woman could endure it.'

Lancelot returned to the city, and started selling the potion and the women came rushing to buy it. Within a few weeks, they all started looking like Twiggy or like the statues in the British Pavilion at Expo, and this made the men of Vancouver most unhappy. One said, 'I married a woman who was fat and warm and comfortable, but now I must share my bedlam and boredom with a talking toothpick.' Another said, 'I do not know about you fellows, but I am leaving for Austria, where women come only in the large economy size.' Another said, 'How can I pat my wife's bottom when she has no bottom left to pat?' The men advanced in a body upon Lancelot and took his potions away and threw them into False Creek; and the women put back all the weight they had lost, and lived hippily ever after.

Lancelot had made a fortune, of course, so he performed his final chivalrous act by seeking out the fire-breathing princess and marrying her and settling down in the British Improprieties. They have two children, Ronson and Shishkebab, and are reasonably happy, but she is getting just a little bored with his knightly attentions.

He loves me, he loves me not

nce upon a time when women wore nylon stockings, there was a delightful young lady named Minnie Maxicoat. Like most single young ladies in Toronto, she went out with various men, but wasn't greatly attracted to any one of them. They were men-type men, colour them grey, and every woman knows exactly what I mean by that.

One day, Minnie was walking down Yonge Street when a little old lady in tennis shoes accosted her, saying, 'Hey sister, give me a buck for a drink!' Annoyed by such rudeness, Minnie brushed her aside, which caused the little old lady to cry after her, 'All right, my proud beauty, you'll pay for this, I'll put a hex on you!' Minnie shrugged her shoulders and forgot about the whole thing, until she noticed people staring in amusement at her. Stopping by a mirror, she found out why. There was a huge pigeon riding along on her head.

Minnie drove the bird away, only to find it in her apartment when she got home, busy soiling her armchair, chesterfield and broadloom. Nor was that all. A fire was blazing in her kitchen, the toilet had flooded over, and a telegram had been delivered announcing that her parents were on the way from Lower East Dudgeon, N.S., for a two-week visit. Minnie thought of the little old lady on Yonge Street, but dismissed the idea of a hex as superstition.

As Minnie rode to work on the subway the next morning, she again found people staring at her, and fished out her mirror to learn why. There, on the end of her nose, was a pimple as big and red as a cherry. 'Damn!', she said, with such emphasis that one of her contacts popped out and she had to scrabble around for it on her hands and knees. Getting to work, she found her watch was wrong, and she was two hours late.

After Minnie's boss had finished bawling her out, she developed an uncontrollable case of hiccoughs, which was most embarrassing when the bank phoned to tell her she was $675 overdrawn. 'That does it!' thought Minnie, and she spent her noon hour walking up and down Yonge Street till she finally found the little old lady. 'Ha, ha!' cackled the witch (for such she was), 'I suppose you're now willing to give me a dollar for a drink?' Minnie took out a $10 bill, saying, 'Here, buy yourself a whole bottle, but just call off that hex.'

The little old lady danced with glee. 'That's enough for a crock of Crown Royal. Okay, Minnie, the hex is off, and furthermore I will grant you two wishes – any two wishes you want.' Minnie thought carefully, 'I want a man who will love me passionately and devotedly, a man who will worship the very ground I tread on, a man who will be madly jealous of me, who will want to be with me every moment. That's my first wish, now as for the second –'

The witch cackled, revealing a row of jagged, black teeth. 'Stop right there, Minnie; you had better save your second wish; you might need it some day.' Minnie went back to work, to find her whole life had changed. The pimple was gone, the bank phoned back to say there had been a mistake, her boss apologized for bawling her out and gave her a bunch of flowers. Most important of all, a man named Lorenz Liebeskrank dropped into the office and recognized her from high school days, and invited her out for dinner.

Lorenz, it soon turned out, was the madly, passionately, insanely jealous lover promised her by the witch. The first thing he told her was, 'Are you seeing any other men besides me? If so, you must get rid of them. You're so gorgeous that I want you all to myself,' and this made Minnie ecstatically happy. The next day, he phoned her, and again took her out for dinner, saying this time, 'I really must insist that you have dinner with me every night; otherwise some other man might try to lure you away from me, and then of course I would have to kill him, or you, or myself, or possibly all three of us.'

Minnie thought, 'This is wonderful, it's like something out of the movies.' It pretty soon came about that she had lunch and dinner with Lorenz every day of the week, and that he phoned her every hour on the hour, getting quite miffed if her line was busy, and making her swear she had not been talking to another man. The time came when he started following her, and standing guard outside her apartment house looking up at the window, and calling her at three and four in the morning to ask if she was alone.

At this point, she protested a little, which caused Lorenz to say, 'But Minnie, darling, don't you understand? It's because I love you so much. When you aren't with me, I'm in utter torment, thinking that some other man may be trespassing on my property, because that is what you are. I love you, and so you belong to me, and I know what is best for you.'

Minnie began to feel that she was being boxed in; she began to resent the way Lorenz bombarded her with questions about where she had been, and what she had done; she began to be scared of his angry outbursts when he saw her even standing beside another man at a cocktail party. The end came when her brother took her out for a drink. Just as they were being served, Lorenz came storming into the bar, pulled Minnie's brother out of his seat and slugged him, saying, 'You leave my woman alone!'

'That does it,' thought Minnie; and she raced down Yonge Street looking for the witch, who on seeing her again, remarked, 'I somehow thought you'd be back. Wasn't I right in telling you to hang on to your second wish?' Minnie said, 'You were, indeed; now my wish is that you replace that jealous, possessive monster with a man who will love me in a nice, easy-going way, letting me be myself and do as I please.'

The witch nodded. 'Good as done,' she replied, and Minnie went home to see what would happen next. The phone rang, and a melodious masculine voice said, 'Good evening, may I speak with Dulcie Farniente?' Minnie said, 'I am sorry, but you have the wrong number,' and was about to hang up when the caller said, 'Oh I don't know, I might have the right number. You have a pleasant voice, and I'm getting bored with Dulcie anyhow, so why don't you come out for dinner with me?'

Realizing her second wish was being granted, Minnie said carefully, 'You have a pleasant voice, too, but I don't even know your name,' at which her mysterious caller identified himself as Franz Freiheit. Minnie asked, 'When and where will we go to dinner?' Franz replied in an offhand manner, 'Oh, I don't give a damn. Tonight, tomorrow night, next week, next month, I'm easy.' Minnie thought, 'You are a bit too easy for my liking,' but went on to settle a time and place with him.

Franz Freiheit turned out to be good-natured, well-mannered, and pleasant in every way but with a casualness toward life that Minnie found at once amusing and annoying. When she said to him after dinner, 'Would you like to come up to my place for a nightcap?' he said, 'Thanks, but I'll take a rain check on it; I feel like cleaning up some work at the office,' and sent her home in a taxi.

At their next meeting, she told him all about Lorenz, saying, 'But you're quite different, you don't seem to be the jealous, domineering type.' Franz replied, 'My dear Minnie, if I love a woman, it is utterly immaterial to me what she does. She can sleep with the Russian Army, she can go out with the entire male staff of Dominion Insecurities, she can spend the weekend in Winnipeg with some other guy, or with eight other guys, come to that. She must live her own life, just as I live my own.'

Minnie said, 'But if a man really loves a woman, doesn't he want to possess her just a little bit?' Franz said, 'My experience in life has shown me the folly of trying to possess another person in any way; also the folly of allowing oneself to be possessed by them. I am not accountable to you for anything, nor you to me; that's the way it is, and that's the way it's going to keep on being.'

Hiding her anger as best she could, Minnie thought, 'He doesn't care about me, he doesn't care about anybody,' and sulked for two whole weeks until he phoned saying, 'Hi, Minnie, haven't seen you for ages; let's go out for a gorgeous dinner tonight.' Minnie thought to herself, 'Theory is one thing, practice is another; I will give him the acid test.'

At dinner Minnie told Franz an invented story about meeting another man, and going to Montreal with him, and what a wonderful lover he was, which caused Franz to pat her hand, saying, 'Now you have at least two men who dote on you, and quite rightly, too. What you need and deserve is twenty-two, assuming you haven't got them already.'

'That does it,' Minnie thought. She rushed out of the restaurant and over to Yonge Street, where she once again found the witch, who said, 'Don't speak a word, I was expecting you. You got your first wish, you got your second, and they both blew up in your face. Ho hum, that's the way it goes. Now let's settle down in some cozy bar, and the two of us can get smashed out of our minds,' and so they did, and for all I know they are still there today.

But never a one for me

ime was when telegrams were delivered by hand to your door, which gave you an opportunity to faint and be revived with smelling salts, but in our prosaic age they are generally delivered by telephone. The telegraph companies use very polite young ladies for this purpose; and once had such a girl named Audrey O'Visual.

The part Audrey disliked about her job was telephoning bad news – for example, telling a married man that his wife had cut short her Bermuda holiday and was flying home immediately; or telling a single woman that her mother was on her way from Charlatan Place to visit her in the big city and make her a few home-cooked meals and meet all her interesting friends.

The part Audrey liked about her job was telephoning good news – for example, advising a man that his son had been expelled from university and would have to start working for a living; or informing a woman that her rich old uncle in St. Catastrophe's had been eaten alive by army web worms.

There was one part of her job which Audrey both liked and disliked – telephoning affectionate messages sent by men to women or by women to men or (this being Toronto) by men to men. Audrey liked this because it made the recipient so happy; she disliked it because she herself never got any such messages.

One day, Audrey telephoned a lady in Willowdale and read her a particularly delightful message: 'How can anyone say God is dead when He brings such a beautiful creature as you into existence?' The recipient sighed, 'Oh, isn't that nice; who did you say it was from?'; to which Audrey answered, 'It is signed simply, Charles;' and the lady at the other end said: 'Charles? Oh, of course, Charles; yes, you may mail the telegram to me.'

A couple of days later, Audrey telephoned a lady in Don Mills to read her a telegram which said, 'The sun rises in the morning so it can shine on you, and sets at night so the moon can have its turn.' Here again, the message was signed simply Charles. A couple of days after that, Audrey telephoned still another message from Charles to still another lady in the Toronto area, this one reading, 'You have two homes – one in Mimico and the other in my heart.'

Audrey started watching the messages from Charles, every one of which, she observed, went to a different woman – 'For a man who loves a beautiful woman like you, every day is a celebration' – 'When you are in Rexdale, who wants to go to the moon?' – 'My head knows that being human, you are imperfect; my heart knows that, being you, you are perfect in every way.'

'Curiouser and curiouser,' thought Audrey. 'Is this Charles a sex fiend or what? Even in these terrible times, a man would scarcely carry on affairs with 187 women simultaneously and at once. I must look into this.' Defying all the company's rules (what are rules to a woman?), she rummaged in various files till she got the name, address and telephone number of one Charles Checkpoint. Further defying the rules, she rang him, saying, 'Is that Mr. Charles Checkpoint? I am Miss Audrey O'Visual from the telegraph company, and I want to know why you are misleading and deceiving half the female population of Metropolitan Toronto. You must take me to lunch at Ed's Squarehouse tomorrow, or I will report you to the police.'

Charles quickly agreed to this, and told her at lunch the next day, 'I am a naturally affectionate man, and I have to express that affection, but like, well, there just isn't anyone,' at which Audrey heard the Vienna Philharmonic under Herbert von Karajan playing the waltz theme from *Der Rosenkavalier*. He continued, 'So I simply chose those women's names at random from the telephone directory; I don't know any of them.'

Audrey answered, 'That is all very well, but how do you explain the fact that every woman accepted the telegram you sent her? Not one suggested there might have been some mistake.' Charles replied, 'No woman getting an affectionate message would deny it was for her, even though it were signed by King Kong or Cardinal Richelieu or Chef Boy-ar-dee; she would automatically accept it, then puzzle over it later. Now take you, Miss O'Visual – what would you do if you got an affectionate telegram signed just, Charles, at your place of employment?'

Audrey blushed, and went back to her office, and within a matter of hours a telegram was delivered to her, reading, 'You have turned my winter into spring, my humble room into the Taj Mahal, and my $120 Bill Brady suit into the robes of an emperor. Come live with me and be my love. Charles.' Yes, the two are snuggled together in a bungalow at Apoplexy Acres with three children, two cats and a gerbil; and so happy is their lot that they are giving serious consideration to getting married.

Take, oh take those lips away

ll of us (said the man at the bar) are addicted to something. Many poor souls, alas, are addicted to drink, others to tobacco, and others to reading the labels on tubes and bottles. I hear tell that the students have all manner of weird addictions; such as smoking catnip, sniffing nail-polish remover, and mixing white port with lemon juice. My own addiction is (I hope, was) a specially insidious one, which caused me only this evening to join R.A.

You don't know what R.A. is? Good heavens, let me explain. It's the shortened name of an organization called Romantics Anonymous, which tries to cure men who are addicted to women and women who are addicted to men. No, we don't touch any of that in-between stuff. R.A. recognizes that the only people who can beat this terrible addiction are those who really want to beat it, and are willing to help others do the same. People like me, in short; for I must tell you that my infatuation with women has broken my health, dissipated my life savings, and caused the collapse of my seven marriages.

That's why I went to the church basement tonight, signed up with R.A. and attended the subsequent meeting. The chairman, a genial fellow named Bill, explained how R.A. works. When a man feels the uncontrollable desire for female companionship, he phones R.A., and they send one of the fellows over to play chess with him, or discuss the latest speech by Robert Nixon, or get him stoned to the point where the only thing in the world he wants is another drink. In the case of a woman overcome with the desire for male companionship, R.A. sends two other women over to play bridge, compare detergents, swap recipes for chocolate chip cookies, or pop their minds with domestic sherry.

The speaker of the evening came next, a fellow named Jack. He told us that he once held a high position in advertising, but then started taking women out for lunch – you know, half-hour lunches at first, then an hour, then two hours. He'd come back to the office around three, and waste the rest of the afternoon writing letters to them and doodling their names on bits of paper.

Pretty soon, his mornings were shot, too; he would spend them going to see women in their offices, and taking them flowers and desk-top dolls and all such hogwash. After he was fired, he went all the way downhill and wound up being supported by an airline stewardess who locked him in her apartment when she took off for High Dudgeon, Sask., or Lower East Uptight, N.B.

A blonde woman in the front row listened intently as Jack spoke, occasionally dabbing at her eyes. It turned out that her name was Mary and she was the other speaker of the evening. Mary said, 'What R.A. has done for me can be summed up in one sentence. I haven't been with a man for two years,' which brought a great burst of applause from the men and women R.A. members both. Mary told us how she started off just going out with one man, then there were two, and in the end she had them by the dozen. Her standards kept slipping too, from book-makers and bootleggers at first, then all the way down to lawyers, politicians and newspapermen.

Mary's desperate craving (so she told us) led her to take up with men who dyed their hair, men who smoked between courses, men who told jokes about people who stammered. She went out with men who said 'God bless' and 'Mamma mia' and 'Sit ye doon' and 'Don't take any wooden nickels' and 'You'd better believe it' and 'You've gotta be kidding.'

She went out with men who saved their pennies for tipping; who got amorous on one beer; who described in detail the terrific putt they made on the 14th green. She went out with men who used the swizzle stick to clean their nails; with men who dug her in the ribs; with men who liked to run their fingers through her wig; with men who wept before, during and after. She went out with a man who could neither read nor write, so had to support himself by teaching English at a community college.

Mary concluded, 'But that's all in the past. I know now that I've kicked the habit; never again will I touch another man.' There was a solid five minutes of hand-clapping, the meeting was over, and I wandered over to this bar, where I have so far had eight double Scotches. Don't worry, old boy, I can take it or leave it, and I really do need just one more to make up for that disgusting sight at the table next to us.

Don't look now, but he's holding her hand and occasionally patting her cheek. He's writing silly notes and giving them to her folded up, and then she opens them and smiles and writes one back. He's lighting cigarettes for her and letting her blow out the match. The filth, the rottenness, I'd like to smash their stupid heads together. But I can't very well, in fact they're looking over at us, and I'd better speak a civil word to them. Hello, Jack; hello, Mary.

'TIS THE SEASON TO BE JELLY

A Christmas carillon

All – well, nearly all – the employers in downtown Toronto are indulgent toward their secretaries; buying them flowers, taking them out to lunch, introducing them to rich, attractive young bachelors, and at least once a week giving them the afternoon off to go shopping. But there was at one time an employer who outdid them all. He was a corporation lawyer named Ebenezer Scruple, his secretary was a young thing named Roberta Scratchit, and he treated her as if she were the only woman on earth.

The other downtown secretaries envied Roberta madly, and made snide remarks about her, such as, 'She probably started sleeping with him even before she got the job,' or, 'Everybody knows he's just paying her off to keep quiet about his income tax evasion;' or, 'Any man who treats a woman that handsomely is covering up for the fact he's a fag from Faggotville, P.Q. You mark my words, there'll be headlines in the paper some day – Steam Baths Raided; Q.C. Faces Grave Charge.' In reality, Ebenezer Scruple was that rare phenomenon, a genuinely good and honest man, an asset to the fine old firm of Replevin, Scruple, Tortfeasor and Cohen. As for Roberta Scratchit, well, we'll see about her later on.

Like any woman, Roberta took full advantage of her employer's kindliness and trust. She would telephone him at 10 a.m., saying, 'Ebbie baby, I have this utterly ghastly head cold, my eyes are streaming like those of an $18,000-a-year M.L.A. bewailing the plight of the poor, and Roman Catholics armed with long knives are chasing Huguenots all up and down my duodenum, so I don't think I can come to work today. I feel just awful thinking of the telephone ringing and the letters piling up and you having to do everything yourself. I really will be on hand bright and early tomorrow.' Ebenezer would say, 'Now, Roberta, you must go straight back to bed and look after yourself; I refuse to let you come back until you have completely recovered,' at which Roberta would thank him profusely, then put on her clothes to go skiing.

Or again, she would walk into his office saying, 'Ebbie, you dear good man, I must see my dentist this afternoon and have a filling replaced, and I just dread the pain . . .' at which he would interrupt, saying, 'You poor child, I insist that you take the rest of the day off and here is some money to go home in a cab afterwards,' which of course she took, and then used it to go and see *Tedium Cool* or *Sleazy Rider* or *A Horrid Couple* or *Paralysis Restaurant*.

Still again, Roberta would say to Ebenezer, 'Oh drat and botheration! Today is my dear old mother's birthday, and I meant to go to the bank and take out some money to buy her a present, but now it's too late. Would you take my cheque for $10?' Her employer would laugh, saying, 'Now, Roberta, don't bother writing me a cheque, here's $20 so you can buy your mother something really smashing, such as a disc of Lawrence Welk conducting the Mormon Tabernacle Choir in a massed rendition of "All You Need Is Love".' Roberta would grab the money with both hands, and rush off to buy herself some Scotch at Honest John's.

It was at Christmas, however, that Ebenezer Scruple outdid himself. Other bosses in downtown Toronto would give their unfortunate secretaries a potted poinsettia, or a two-pound box of Laura Discords. But Ebenezer handled this, as everything else, in the grand manner of a Cyrano de Bergerac, giving Roberta a mink coat, or a two-way air ticket to Hawaii, or a week in the West Indies, or a block of International Pickle.

Nor was that all. On December 1, he always said to her, 'Now, Roberta, since you are the most attractive woman in Toronto, you must have many men friends; and since you have many men friends, you will need to buy presents for all of them; and since you need to buy presents for all of them, you will need the time to select them, so I will not expect you back in the office until Christmas Eve, when I will give you your own present.'

One Christmas Eve, Ebenezer gave Roberta a present which even she found surprising – a cheque for $1,000. Weeping with joy, she told him, 'I do declare, Ebenezer Scruple, you're the jolliest old elf in Metropolitan Toronto, or at any rate on lower Bay Street,' then rushed out to deposit it while he locked up the office, and went home thinking, 'She is such a good, sweet, loyal girl that she deserves the happiest Christmas and New Year's ever.'

That night, Ebenezer knocked back a few ounces of Crown Royal, watched the Dean Martins do a program on the joys of family life, and retired to bed, where on the stroke of midnight a spectre suddenly appeared before him. 'Ebenezer Scruple, Q.C., it is my painful duty to inform you that Miss Roberta Scratchit, better known on lower Bay Street as Roadside Mabel, is not such a good, sweet girl as like what you think she is. There will be a brief pause for thirty consecutive commercials; following which you will behold in full colour certain events relating to Christmas past, Christmas present and Christmas yet to come.'

In the vision of Christmas past, Ebenezer beheld his secretary having a cosy little dinner with one of the younger lawyers who worked for Replevin, Scruple, Tortfeasor and Cohen. He was saying to her, 'What do you really think of Mr. Scruple?' at which Roberta grimaced, 'Oh, that old creep, blecchh! He's always looking down the front of my dress and making coy remarks about miniskirts and deliberately pushing past me when I lean over my desk. And then, all of a sudden, he makes a great big pass at me, pow! With Mr. Tortfeasor, you at least get some advance notice; he starts clearing his throat and patting his sideburns. But not our Ebbie; oh no, he comes down like a wolf on the fold, woof, woof. Tell me, Hugo, isn't there some age when men get over it, like 45 or 50? Should I start putting saltpetre in his coffee?'

Ebenezer awoke in horror, crying: 'Lies, lies, lies!' Then he dreamed again and saw the vision of Christmas present – the way in which Roberta was planning to spend the $1,000 cheque he had given her. She was lying on the Jamaican beach with an athletic young man, who was caressing her in a manner more to be imagined than described; and was murmuring to him, 'I have it all figured out, Gunther. My repulsive boss, Ebenezer Scruple, has a secret file in his office labelled Political Payoffs, Bribery, Corruption, Simony, Nepotism, Indulgences, etc. I will sneak it out and have the contents xeroxed, then sell them around Queen's Park and City Hall for what they will fetch. The old fool will never catch on until you and I are safely in Buenos Aires.'

Again, Ebenezer awoke, screaming, 'Roberta, baby, what are you doing to me?' Yet again he slept and dreamed, beholding the vision of Christmas yet to come. Roberta Scratchit had stuffed a pillow inside her see-through crochet dress and was standing before the president of the

34

firm, Reinhardt Replevin, with tears running down her face into his cut-glass ashtray. 'Oh yes, Mr. Replevin, I was a pure and innocent girl when I came to work for Ebenezer Scruple, and now I have been most foully seduced, betrayed, abandoned and left with egg on my face. Yes, none other than he or him is the father of my unborn child! Shall I bring public contumely on Replevin, Scruple, Tortfeasor and Cohen by telling the awful story to the newspapers? Or would you rather buy me off for some reasonable amount such as $50,000?'

Ebenezer Scruple awoke with a jolt and screamed and leaped out of bed. Six o'clock of a Christmas morning! It wasn't too late, there was still time. He ran to the telephone and dialled Roberta Scratchit, who answered sleepily, 'Is that you, Ronnie? Come on over and climb in with me, my poor little feet are cold.'

Ebenezer laughed, saying, 'No, Miss Scratchit, it is not Ronnie, neither is it Lon Chaney nor J. Edgar Hoover nor Engelbert Humperdinck nor Bobby Breen nor Brian Boru nor Sir Joseph Porter, K.C.B. It is your creepy old boss, Ebenezer Scruple, calling to say that you're fired and that I've issued a stop-payment order on that $1,000 cheque. Ho, ho, ho! Bah, Humberside Collegiate!' And he cackled so loudly that all the escalators in the subway system started functioning.

Now let us sing:
'Tis the season to be jelly

Christmas wouldn't be Christmas without any pretense – for example, the ridiculous claim of Dietrich Doppelganger to be the reincarnation of Napoleon Bonaparte, when everybody knows that I am. Doppelganger also claims to be the editor of the *Mop and Pail,* which in turn claims to be Canada's national newspaper. Ha! Ask for it in Moosomin, Sask., and they'd probably direct you to the hardware store. Ha!

The editorial writers have long since taken D.D.'s measure; and it amused me to overhear a group of them talking about him last night. One spat as he remarked, 'Doppelganger is all heart transplant. He'd give you the shirt off his back if it needed laundering. When he goes to see his mother at Christmas, he takes presents not just for her but for everyone else in the poorhouse. Doppelganger doesn't discriminate; he dispenses even-handed injustice to everybody, regardless of face, choler or greed. With him every day is the dawn of a new error. To sum up, I don't like him and I don't like his authorized Ski-Doo dealer.'

Another remarked, 'Doppelganger really gets me riled up with his snide remarks about our beloved Queen; I'm sure her friendship with Disraeli is perfectly respectable.' Still another said, 'I can't understand why he's so enthusiastic about the North-West Expedition. You mark my words, Lewis and Clark will be lucky to get as far as Omaha.' A fourth cried, 'What's all this nonsense he talks about harnessing the power of the atom? Man will no more do that than fly to the moon.'

Finally one of the writers piped up, 'You fellows can run down D.D. all you like, but I'm not taking any chances; I've just got thirty-three years to go before my pension. Besides, it's Christmas Eve, and he'll soon be calling us in to give us our presents.' A chorus of jeers drowned him out as the writers listed some of the gifts they'd received from Father Crime at previous Ghoultides – a hula hoop; a stuffed cormorant; a 1928 Manitoba licence plate; a one-way ticket to Easter Island; an autographed picture of Pola Negri; a 78 r.p.m. record of Kate Smith singing 'When the Moon Comes Over Mount Forest'; the collected speeches of Senator Andrew Thompson; Volume I of the *Rowell-Sirois Report.*

Disregarding their chatter, I went to see Captain Blight in person, making my usual stormy entry: 'Gleason's bleatings! Morbid Christmas and a hopeless New Year! Kingsville is for the birds; all Flesherton is on grass; the twentieth century belongs to cannibalism. Did you hear about the police breaking up that Yorkville wedding? There were too many hims in the service. Your face looks like the intersection of the 401 and Highway 27. Do you like Kipling? I don't know, I never kippled. The stock market's all mixed up, they don't know whether they're Cominco or Boeing, but such is the price we must pay for our bazoom-and-borscht economy. Join the struggle for the liberation of Saskatchewan! Have your eyes ever been checked? No, they've always been blue. The twentieth century belongs to cannabis. Help keep our city clean, have a pigeon for lunch. The International Conference on Apathy was a smashing success; nobody turned up.'

Doppelganger sighed heavily. 'How can you be so frivolous when the Senate Committee on Poverty has just revealed that poor people make less money than rich people? Nor is that my only cause for concern. I am irked beyond all endurance by this endless fighting in the Middle East; why can't the Christians make some kind of peace with the Saracens? As for those anti-draft demonstrations in the States, I think Lincoln should show more firmness. Student activism is all very well, R.J., but this lad Gabriel Prinzep is carrying it just a bit too far. On top of all which there's the outbreak of parthenogenesis in Lennox and Addington County, and persistent reports that Britain is planning to withdraw from Britain. For shame, my boy. If John Diefenbaker were still alive, he'd turn over in his grave.'

I floated away, and shortly heard Honest Edsel screeching at the editorial writers (the Clod Squad or Fink Tank, as I call them) to receive their presents – 'Come along, now, Sidbec, you don't have to prostrate yourself before me, kneeling is quite good enough.' When Sidbec returned, tears of gratitude were streaming down his face. 'After getting my present,' he cried, 'I take back all I said against Doppelganger. He's given me a three-year subscription to the *Saturday Evening Post*.'

Povwar was equally joyous when he reeled out. 'Doppelganger told me the *Mop and Pail* is planning to open a bureau at Wawa, and I'll be in full charge of it for the first five years. Then he told me that the official symbol of Wawa is an enormous goose, and then he fell out of his chair laughing. I don't quite understand the joke, but I do appreciate the high honour.' Corfam came out clutching an empty bottle. 'Doppelganger is so kind and generous. This bottle once contained a loathsome substance called Scotch, but he drank all of it himself so as to save me from its harmful effects. He is a true saint.' Domtar emerged with stars in his eyes, crying to the other writers, 'I own a piece of Canada! Now tell me, fellows, just whereabouts is Chesterfield Inlet?'

My own name was called at last. Doppelganger explained, 'I always leave you to the end, R.J., because you're one of the seedier members of our staff, not to mention being our oldest inhibited. Now would you like to guess what St. Knucklehead has for you in his bag of Toyotas?' I yawned. 'An Alpenhorn? Misfortune cookies? A cut-glass inkwell? A set of tire chains? A used typewriter ribbon? A scale model of the *Bonaventure*? A guide to the Stoney Creek traffic circle? A letter of introduction to Tom Kent? A Swahili-Eskimo dictionary? An invitation to the Orillia premiere of *I Am Curious – Yellow*? A nuclear fallout shelter? A face towel with the mysterious inscription C.P.R.?'

D.D. guffawed, showing all thirty-six teeth. 'It's true, R.J., I've had my sport with you in the past, but this year I'm playing it straight. The management really does appreciate hard work, and in this small white envelope you'll find a token of our esteem, which we trust you'll use for travel to glamorous places.' Going back to the office, I opened it with trembling hands; inside was a tiny piece of metal bearing the imprint of the Toronto Transit Commission; and as I heard Doppelganger's coarse bellow of joy, I realized I had once again snatched defeat from the jaws of victory.

Yvonne and Old Kris

Even saints have been known to lose their cool – and this is what happened one time with, of all people, Santa Claus. He remarked to his wife, Sandra Claus, 'I have had it right up to the ears and eyebrows and am seriously thinking of chucking this whole Christmas caper.' Sandra looked at him anxiously, and he explained:

'It's the elves. They spend 25 per cent of their time making toys in the factory, 25 per cent making moonshine in the kitchen, 25 per cent making trouble in the union hall and 25 per cent making out in the snowdrifts. It's the reindeer. They are tired of this Dancer, Prancer bit – that's too common for them – they want hoity-toity names like Elmira's Folly and Tartarin de Tarascon and Sweet Nell of Old Drury.

But mostly it's the children – writing me mawkish letters about how good they've been all year long when in fact they have reduced their teachers to chewing the chalk and their parents to biting the broadloom. And it's Santa, give me this; Santa, give me that. When did any of the little creeps ever give Santa anything? No, I'm splitting the scene this year.'

Sandra, being a wise woman, didn't fuss, but sat down and wrote to Rasputin J. Novgorod, a gentleman of advanced years who churned out a daily newspaper column in a faraway city called Toronto. Reading over her letter, the old man tugged at the Henry VIII beard which had caused him to be barred from half the high schools in Southern Ontario. He muttered to himself, 'We have indeed fallen upon parlous times when Kris theatens not to make with the Kringle. But what can I do? How can I, a humble writer of liquorary muster-passers, change Santa's mind?'

Little did Novgorod realize that he and Sandra and the children of the world had something going for them in the person of a Toronto high school student known to all, and especially to her hapless parents and teachers, as Yvonne the Terrible.

At the tender age of sixteen, Yvonne was already a one-woman disaster area. She shaved her legs with her father's razor, cleaned her comb with her mother's toothbrush and at 4 in the morning turned her phonograph on full blast with recordings by Ebbie Scrooge and His Three Spirits, or Pierre Trudeau and the Drunken Sailors, or Topsy Topless and the Double Exposures.

Yvonne liked to alarm her mother by going into the bathroom several mornings in a row and pretending to retch violently. She liked to annoy her father by spending three hours on the telephone when he was waiting for an important long distance call from the president of his company. When her parents had guests, she would come rushing in and scream, 'There's a great big cockroach chasing me all around the kitchen!'

Yvonne dressed like a bad trip. She wore hip-high boots of bright yellow vinyl and earrings with Stop and Go lights and sun glasses as big as cartwheels and a sweater so long she kept falling over it. She referred to her father as the Bore of 1812 and to her mother as the Old Grey

Square. She would gorge herself on potato chips all afternoon, then announce that she wasn't hungry when the family sat down to a laboriously prepared meal of roast Dief with Yorkville pudding and mashed pedestrians.

As for her teachers, Yvonne harried them with a cunning and ferocity that would have done credit to a much older woman. She would tell the other students at Barbed Wire Secondary, 'Miss Bulgebelly's purse flew open today and a strange object rolled out – something like a cigarette, but much thinner and tightly packed with green tobacco.' Or she would tell them, 'Mr. Bottlenose certainly gets along well with the boys and is always laying his arm carelessly around their shoulders.'

She drew lurid pictures of teachers engaged in sex orgies and printed them on the school Xerox and sold them for 25 cents each. She charged a dollar for doctoring report cards, and two dollars for producing essays cribbed from the lesser known works of G. K. Chesterton. She pulled the fire alarm when the basketball team was in the showers.

As Christmas rolled around, Yvonne sat down to write her customary letter to Santa, telling him how virtuous she had been all year and making her customary request – a Wicked Uncle who would liberate her from her crummy school and her crummy parents and take her with him (and, quite possibly, his mistress) on a year-long trip around the world. 'Dear Santa,' she started to write, but then she heard angels twanging on their harps and tootling on their trumpets and realized that even she could not go through with such a monstrous piece of mendacity, and she started to cry so hard that she made a puddle on the floor in which her false eyelashes floated pathetically.

Yvonne said to herself: 'There is only one thing to do and that is to go down to *The Goad and Flail* and see Mr. Novgorod, who is the patron quaint of us rotten, irresponsible teenagers.' She found him snarling and snuffling over his immense collection of Air Canada boarding passes.

The patriarch listened attentively as Yvonne explained that she couldn't bring herself to tell the usual lies to Santa. As she spoke, Novgorod thought: 'That's the answer. Here's the opportunity to do the one good deed of my delightfully misspent life.' He grinned all over his withered features and, when Yvonne had finished speaking, remarked, 'Why not tell Santa the truth? Tell him you're a rotten kid who doesn't deserve a present. Send him one instead. He'll probably be so amazed by your honesty that he'll let you have the Wicked Uncle you crave.' Yvonne said, 'But what can I give Santa?'

'That's easy,' Novgorod replied. 'Send him a year's subscription to *The Goad and Flail*. I can just see him up there at the North Pole reading the latest headlines – Pompeii Tackles Air Pollution Problem; Christians, Saracens Clash in Middle East; Roman Leader Stabbed on Senate Steps; Slum Clearance Plan Fails, Guy Fawkes Arrested; Teacher Convicted on Morals Charge, Drinks Hemlock.'

Between them Novgorod and Yvonne worked out a letter which went thus and as follows: 'Santa Baby: My name is Yvonne the Terrible, and what I would like for Christmas is a Wicked Uncle who will take me around the world. But you mustn't give him to me – you mustn't give me any presents at all, because I am a rotten kid who doesn't deserve one. Don't bring me anything, Santa baby, not even a warm pair of woolly gloves. Instead I am sending you a Christmas present and hoping it will bring you happiness every morning of the year.' Both cackled with glee as they mailed it.

When Santa read the letter, he started to blubber, saying, 'Well, bless my Yea, Rifles buttons. What a fool I have been! How can I split the scene when a pure and generous child like Yvonne speaks to me from the depths of her warm little heart? Start packing my bags and harnessing the reindeer, Sandra. It's going to be Christmas as usual.'

Yes, dear old Santa took presents to all the children of the world and especially to Yvonne the Terrible. Early on Christmas morning, she got up and went downstairs and found under the tree the recumbent figure of a handsome, well dressed man. 'Who are you?' she asked. To which he replied: 'I am your Wicked Uncle from Saskatchewan, where I made a huge fortune by selling my birthright for a mess of potash. I got your father and mother royally sloshed last night, in the course of which they gave their permission for you and me to travel around the world with a delightful lady named Gretchen Gemuetlich, who will instruct you in such womanly arts as Elementary Home-Breaking, Intermediate Motel Registering, Advanced Scene Making and Conversational Perfidy.'

They went out to the airport, where Yvonne telephoned Mr. Novgorod to thank him and wish him a merry Christmas. But all she got was a somewhat slurred masculine voice which said: 'I am sorry to tell you that Mr. Novgorod has departed this world. He perished yesterday from a tart attack. He was gunned down at the Shediac Mobster Festival. The students at Prince Edward C. I. killed him and ate him and threw his bones in the Bay of Quinsy. His last words were thus and as follows: 'God help us, every one.'

Home for Christmas

ell me, sir (said the man at the bar), which in your opinion is better? To spend Christmas alone, in a furnished room here in Toronto; or to spend it back home in Alberta, with your family around you? You know the answer, of course; and so do I; but I had it somewhat forcibly impressed upon me last week.

I will relate the story, but first of all let me buy you a drink. This is gin-and-tonic; Acadian Old Vic, to be precise, and I'm getting rather attached to it. After the first drink, you believe Communist China exists; after the second, you believe Mitchell Sharp exists; after the third, you believe Robert Stanfield exists, and it's probably wise to stop at that point.

And now to Christmas. Being a peaceful soul, I have never married; fighting, name-calling and the hurling of alarm clocks do not appeal to me, though I agree they have an irresistible charm to many. Accordingly, I live in a rooming-house near the corner of Lurch and Wesley.

My practice on Christmas Eve is to sit in my humble room, have two or three pleasant drinks, and turn on the radio so I can listen to the lovely, reverent old commercials. I spend the morning of Christmas Day lying in bed, have lunch at any restaurant I find open, and in the afternoon go for a walk. In the evening, I treat myself to a gracious dinner at Le Provençal, and then whatever movie is showing at the Uptown.

This Christmas, however, was different. My family back in Gopher Gulch flatly insisted I should come and spend it with them. 'It just breaks my heart,' wrote my mother, 'to think of you there in the big, unfriendly city, all alone on the Day of Days.' She enclosed a two-way ticket on the Greyhound bus, and I arrived there Christmas Eve after a delightful and comfortable journey.

I knocked on the door and was greeted by my sister Mary, who immediately brought a beer bottle down on my head. 'Oh, I'm sorry,' she said, 'It's you, Jack. I thought you were my husband, Fred, who hasn't shown his ugly face around home for the last week, and I know perfectly well he's shacked up with that dirty little redhead at some hotel in Calgary. I've been drinking since 10 o'clock this morning, and am stoned to the eyebrows, but come in and maybe you can find a Band-Aid some place to put on your poor bleeding scalp.'

My father and mother have never got along too harmoniously; they stick together for the sake of the Herefords; so I wasn't surprised to find them arguing bitterly in the living room, each recalling some awful thing the other had done in 1921, or had said in 1937. With them was my Social Credit uncle, plainly in the grip of the grape. He was storming away to himself about the international bankers and the Protocols of Zion and how this fellow Darwin should be dismissed from the faculty of the University of Alberta.

My brother Charlie stuck his head around the door. 'Hi, Jack,' he said. 'Welcome home. She's going down to 87 below tonight, but that's a damn sight more comfortable than 45 above in Toronto. It's a dry cold, you don't really feel it –', at which point his left ear fell off. When I'd glued it back on, he told me that my mother had pushed my father into the Christmas tree, setting it on fire and burning all the presents, including my own – the collected speeches of George Drew. 'But it's the spirit of Christmas that counts,' he continued. 'And here we all are at last under the same roof. The family that flays together stays together.' He poured himself a full glass of whisky, drank it in one gulp, and collapsed on the floor.

I got what sleep I could, interrupted by shouts, screams, curses, thuds, crashes of breaking glass, and occasional gunfire. On Christmas morning, I came down to find my sister Mary behaving strangely; she insisted that she was a turkey and that the family were planning to cook and eat her. I rang a famous Edmonton psychiatrist, Dr. Livingstone I. Presume, and asked him to come right away, but was disturbed when he entered the house on all fours, wearing a paper hat and barking like a dog.

'Who's the patient?' said Dr. Presume, and the family all pointed at me. 'It's him,' they said, 'He hasn't got the Christmas spirit.' 'We'll soon fix that,' said the learned man, and started beating me savagely with two enormous red candles. At this point, my Seventh Day Adventist uncle drove his Jaguar straight up the front steps and into the house. The police came roaring in after him, and in the subsequent confusion I escaped, fleeing across the snow-covered prairie till I came to the Trans-Canada Highway and got the bus after a frosty vigil during which I lost three of my toes.

Still, I'm back in Toronto, and that's what counts. I've nothing against Christmas, nothing against family life, either. But I am who I am, and I know what I know. A room of my own; a room with a door, and a lock on the door; do you understand what I mean by that? I think a great many people do. And I don't think all of them are single.

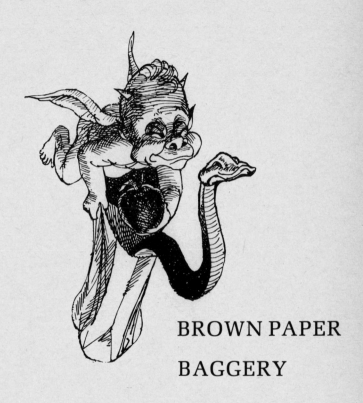

BROWN PAPER

BAGGERY

About as far as they can go

ave you ever observed (said the man at the bar) that the major events in our lives spring from seemingly minor ones? A man goes into a coffee shop to get out of the rain, and there meets his future mistress. Ah, sir, do not shudder; it could have been worse; it could have been a former one. A woman forgets her purse, goes back for it, and misses her plane, which promptly proceeds to explode over the Booze Peninsula. Returning gratefully home, she gets mashed on a safety crosswalk.

It was a seemingly casual incident that brought me my present opulence. As I walked along Yonge Street one day, I noticed a piece of scrap metal on the sidewalk, possibly left over from a drunken brawl between two computers. Worried that some barefoot teeny-bopper might cut herself on its jagged edge, I picked it up, intending to deposit it in the next trash can.

Before I reached one, however, I noticed a mob of people surging into an art gallery. The curiosity which took me along with them was enhanced when I got inside. Hanging from one wall were three tangled wire coathangers. Beside them a label said, 'Love in Lindsay, $85'. A bearded gentleman viewing it told me, 'This is certainly a courageous assault on our atavistic taboos, superstitions and shibboleths. But I think the dichotomy of our civilization is more effectively underscored by that one in the corner' – and he pointed to a Mac's milk jug which had been painted mauve, was entitled 'Soliloquy in Green', and was priced at $110.

I put down my piece of scrap metal on a coffee table, and went to look at other exhibits. When I got back, a group of people were gathered around it, chattering excitedly. One man said to me, 'Is that yours?' I explained I was about to remove it. 'Nonsense!' he cried, fishing for his wallet. 'You've completely captured the alienation of the New Brunswick intellectual. Let's see now, I have only $60 with me in cash, but if you'll take that as a deposit . . .'

I grasped the situation, grabbed his money, and was back the next day with a used toothbrush, a spavined umbrella, a frying pan with three holes punched through the middle, and a bicycle pump which had been run over by a bulldozer. I came away with a fat wad of money in my pocket, and my reputation as an avant-garde sculptor solidly established. Next, I moved into the world of contemporary music where, as I soon observed, the key to success is to combine the maximum of sound and fury with the minimum of comprehensibility.

Recording the announcements made at Toronto International Airport, I ran them backwards, mixing in squeals, honks and jolts from the Vaughan Township freight yards, sound of feeding time at the Riverdale Zoo, rock slides, Mosport, the assembly line at Massey-Ferguson, and the magnificent finale of a grand piano being hurled from the top of Calgary's Husky Tower. After I presented it at a coffee house called the Rhomboid Orgasm, the critics pronounced it a work of pure genius, while unable to agree whether it represented the spring break-up at Short Shrift, Man., or the state of ecumenicalism in Newfoundland.

It remained to have myself acclaimed as a modern poet. Attending recitations in Yorkville, I found that today's bards had renounced not only rhyme and metre but also meaning. You know the sort of thing – 'When imagery becomes ambivalent, leering eggcups frustrate my amnesia.' I went one step further. With rhyme, metre, and meaning gone, why should words remain? I stunned the Yorkville crowd first by giving a poetry recitation which consisted wholly of yawns, shrieks and grunts; next, by giving one where I sat on the stage in complete silence; and finally, by publishing a book of verse in which all the pages were blank. It sold like hot cakes, need I say, leaving fogies like Cohen and Layton green with envy.

Thus, sir, my fortune was made. And what did I do with the money? You'll find out if you come along with me to my house – paintings by Renoir, sculptures by Rodin, the complete works of Beethoven as conducted by Herbert von Karajan. 'A thing of beauty is a thing of joy forever' – wouldn't you agree? Nobody, but nobody, can tell it like John Keats.

Far from the mad In-crowd

nce upon a time, there was a city where the people who earned $5,000 a year were almost as miserable as the ones who earned $10,000; and on the outskirts of this city there were sundry groves and copses; and in one of them there was a hollow tree; and in it there lived a hermit named Peter Pancreas.

Most men become hermits because they hate the human race, but Peter Pancreas was just the opposite. He admired his fellow-men, he wanted to measure up to their high moral standards, and so he was trying to improve himself through contemplation and prayer, following which he planned to rejoin them and perform good works such as throwing down temperance tracts from the top of the Ferris wheel at the C.N.E.

Nobody knew the hermit was in the hollow tree until the day when he was praying so energetically that he set fire to his sackcloth robe, and switched to a string of oaths that would have done credit to a Rexdale teeny-bopper. A man passing by heard the swearing and jumped several feet in the air, and said, 'When the trees start cursing at me, I know it's time to stop mixing brandy with vodka,' and was greatly relieved when the hermit poked his head out of the tree and apologized to him.

News of the hermit got around after this, and people came to see him and speculated on his unusual way of life. Men would say, 'He is probably on the lam from the Metro police, who want to arrest him for parricide, bestiality, and cartnapping.' Women would say, 'Do you suppose he wears anything under that sackcloth robe?'

Men would say, 'I wonder how he manages for money? I myself make $600 a month, and we only have meat twice a week, and then it's

Gravy Train.' Women would say, 'Living all alone like that, he must be starved for romance. If he ever leaps out and attacks me, I will whisper for help.' Men would say, 'He probably has secret tunnels under that tree which lead to the Friar's Tavern, the liquor store, the McGill Street Y.W.C.A., and the Imperial Room at the Royal York.' Women would say, 'Perhaps he has some terrible personal tragedy in his past, such as attending Charlatan University or teaching at Slumber College.'

Things got to the point where people started to demand messages from the hermit, saying, 'There is not much point in all this prayer and contemplation unless something instructive comes out. If Peter Pancreas doesn't measure up to his duty, the authorities should take away his hermit permit.' Accordingly, someone asked him what conclusion he had reached about the birth control pill.

The hermit thought for a while, then replied, 'It is wicked to use the pill unless circumstances justify it, and then it is perfectly all right.' This led some people to say, 'He certainly came out firmly in support of the pill,' and others to say, 'He certainly came out firmly against the pill,' and still others to say, 'The papers will be out tomorrow with a 10,000-word interpretation of what the hermit really meant by that, along with comments by Molly Bloom, Phileas Fogg, Carrie Nation, the Venerable Bede and Charlotte Whitton.'

Gaining confidence, the hermit gave capsule-sermons such as, 'There's so much bad in the worst of us, and so much bad in the best of us, that it ill behooves any of us to speak well of the rest of us.' This caused some people to say, 'It's obvious he must have been married at some point,' and others to say, 'There. I told you he was a native-born Torontonian.' Or the hermit would say. 'Better a dinner of verbs where love is than a stalled Oxford Dictionary and hatred therewith.' Or he would say, 'There remain Percy Faith, Bob Hope and Cary Grant; and the greatest of these is Cary.'

In time, the hermit became a Toronto institution, with people affectionately referring to him as the Maharishi Yogurt. The T.T.C. laid on a special service to his hollow tree, with buses leaving the Islington subway station every three and a half hours; and the crowds which gathered to hear him were almost as large as those which gather outside a Toronto liquor store on the evening before a Christian holiday.

The hermit started off by giving capsule sermons to the crowd, such as 'Man's inhumanity to man makes countless thousands read the morning paper;' or, 'Life is mostly froth and bubble, two things stand like stone; absence in another's trouble, money in one's own.' People enjoyed this for a while, but then (for such is human nature) they demanded more.

The day came when a man said to the hermit, 'Last night, I committed a grievous sin, most enjoyable.' The hermit said, 'Well, what do you want me to do about it?' The man said, 'I want to tell you all about it, naturally, with time, place, and the name of the motel, which as I recall is the Hay, Nonny, Nonny, and where people register under such names as Leon Trotsky, Oliver Goldsmith, Soames Forsyte, and Alexander Graham Bell. After I have confessed all to you, grinning and licking my chops over the spicier details, you must mete out some reasonable punishment to me, and then I can do the whole thing over again.'

The hermit listened carefully to the man's story, gave him a moderate penalty (taking four small children to the C.N.E. on a rainy afternoon), and thus got into the confessional business. Another man said to him, 'I took my dear old mother downtown on the subway yesterday afternoon and pushed her off the top of the Bank of Commerce.' The hermit was shocked. 'You could at least have taken her in a taxi; your punishment will be to spend fifteen minutes listening to Boredom Clinker on CFRB.'

A woman said to the hermit, 'I was unfaithful to my lover last night.' The hermit asked, 'Whom with?' to which the woman angrily replied, 'With my husband, of course; do you think I'm a tart?' The hermit sighed, and ordered her by way of punishment to read the collected speeches of Senator David Crawl.

A high-school student told the hermit, 'Like I was driving my Thunderbird to Massprod Secondary, see, and then I seen the vice-principal bombing along on his bicycle, see, and so I rammed the old buzzard and killed him, see, and then I dumped his body in the lake.' The hermit was indignant, saying, 'Lake Ontario is polluted enough already, without people like you making it worse. Your punishment will be the most severe I can think of – a two-mile walk in the country with your mother, during which she will draw your attention to the birds and the bees, and ask if you would like to have a serious discussion with her along that line.'

A man confessed, 'I took my secretary to New York over the weekend. We checked into the Taft Friday night, and didn't even come out of the room till Sunday night. Would you believe 27 . . .' The hermit sharply cut him off: 'Your punishment will be to drink three cups of Saskatchewan coffee – one for boasting, one for Sabbath-breaking, and one for taking her to the Taft, instead of the Plaza.'

As the hermit listened to all these tales, he began to lose his faith in human goodness. His own goodness started to crumble, too. Pretty soon, he had concealed a recording device in his hollow tree, and was taping some of the jucier confessions. He then sold the tapes to novelists, playwrights, and C.B.C. producers who turned out works based upon them which the critics greeted with such expressions as 'Unflinching realism' and 'Shows profound insight into the moral dilemma of our time'.

Nor was that all. A man or woman would approach the hermit from time to time, saying, 'You must get pretty tired hearing about the same old sins over and over again.' The hermit craftily replied, 'Oh, I don't know; they often come up with a fresh twist on one of the familiar sins, and a couple of them have fascinated me by confessing sins which are absolutely new and different.'

The person inquiring would say, 'New sins? Tell me quick, what are they? I must rush out and commit – oops, I mean, I must try to avoid them.' The hermit then would say, 'Well now, we could have a private consultation about that; and of course, you will make a $50 donation to a fund I have started for the noble purpose of stamping out atheism among divinity students.'

One thing that impressed people about the hermit was the simplicity of his life. They asked, 'Why don't you have a telephone?' to which he replied, 'Send not to know for whom the Bell tolls; it tolls for thee, with the announcement that thou hast just won a free sewing machine, which in the end will cost thee more than if thou had gone to Eaton's and bought one.'

They asked, 'Why do you have no car?' The hermit replied, 'The automobile is simply the means of transporting you, under circumstances of extreme personal danger, from one industrial slum to another precisely like it. The only place worth getting to is Heaven, and you won't find it on the Shell road map.' They asked in awe, 'No TV?' The hermit said, 'I am neither entertained nor uplifted by the spectacle of housewives grinning like apes as they wash the yellow, green, burnt orange and frosted mauve lipstick out of their husbands' shirt collars.'

What struck most people about the hermit's way of living, however, was its serenity – a sharp contrast with the sound and fury of their own

53

environments. The time came when a man said to the hermit, 'I just had a blazing row with my wife, who most viciously accused me of blowing the rent money at the track, when in fact I blew it in the bars. Can I stay in your hollow tree for a while? It's so quiet compared with my home, where all day long the noise of battle rolls.'

The hermit thought about it, then said, 'It is part of the religious tradition to provide sanctuary to those in distress. However, it seems only proper that you should make a donation to the charitable fund I have set up; the money will be used to teach reading, writing, spelling and simple arithmetic to graduates of Ontario high schools.' A deal was made, and the hermit gleefully added the money to the hoard which was making him rich beyond the dreams of Avis.

The next was a woman who told the hermit, 'It's my two teen-age sons, who speak only in clicks, snarls and grunts. They spend all day tending their coiffures, and all night either gunning their Yamahas under my bedroom window or else blasting out records by such groups as the Last Straws, the Sordid Details and the Sickening Thuds. Please let me move into your hollow tree. I don't snore; I don't have nightmares; and I promise not to molest you in any way, on account of having been bored and erased at Picton.'

A man said to the hermit, 'I've been trying to teach English literature to a bunch of gorillas whose only ambitions in life are to seduce the red-headed waitress in the tavern next door, to get a factory job at $3.87 an hour, and to drive a Jag at 110 m.p.h. down the Marat-Sade Freeway. Can I get away from it all in your hollow tree, or must I be formally committed?' A woman said to him, 'It's my creepy husband. When I criticize him for anything, he agrees with me, and says I'm absolutely right, and he's sorry, and will try to do better. Let me stay in your tree for a while while I figure out ways and means to murder the toad.'

People (and money) started streaming into the hermit's abode – children running away from cruel parents who expected them to help with the dishes; women fleeing miserly husbands who wanted to know why an almost invisible pair of shoes should cost $45; men on the lam from wives who nagged and whined to be taken out to dinner once a month; teen-age girls at loggerheads with square old mothers who wouldn't let them smoke cigarillos at the breakfast table.

Pretty soon, of course, there were more of them than the hollow tree could accommodate; and that's why it doesn't exist any more. In its place, if you look hard enough, you will find an immense hotel called

The Hermitage; and you scarcely need to be told who owns and runs it. He's in the lobby much of the time, delivering such gnomic utterances as 'Let sleeping bags lie', and 'You can lead a Norse to Waterloo Lutheran, but you can't make him think', and 'A bird in a hammock is worth two in a bushel basket', and 'Be it ever so mumble, there's no place like Rome.'

Mene, mene, tekel upharsin

I f (said the man at the bar) there are fallen women, aren't there also fallen men? Should we not have associations set up to help these unfortunates, and institutions where they might find sanctuary? I myself, as you may divine, am a fallen man, which is why I sit here drinking this new brand of gin, Schenley's Silver Wedding. One ounce of it and you embrace your bride of twenty-five years; two ounces and you give her a mink stole; three ounces and you try to do her in with the power mower.

Permit me to tell you of my terrible fall, comparable only with that of Lucifer. You will recognize my name, perhaps – Mushmouth McGargle, formerly a professor at the University of Toronto, Canada's largest community of dollars. Like many professors, I did some public speaking on current issues – you know the sort of thing – Do Married Men Make Good Husbands? Why High School Students Are Revolting; What Does Newfoundland Really Want?

My life was simple enough until the fateful morning when I dictated a speech to my secretary, telling her to type it during the afternoon. She unfortunately drank her lunch, reeled back to her Underwood, and produced – as I found to my dismay when I stood up that evening to address the Junior Bored and Staid – a mass of gibberish. There was nothing to do but go through with it. Accordingly, I began:

'By extrapolating the historicity of palimpsests, and conceptualizing noncognitive differentiations, emotive and normative paradigms achieve autochthony.' So it went for three-quarters of an hour, till I wound up: 'In short, the meaning of being must always be predicated on econometric casuality.'

The audience reaction was stunning – ten solid minutes of applause. They lined up afterwards and shook my hand and demanded copies of the speech. One man said he had never heard Canada's constitutional problem so sharply defined, while another remarked, 'It's good to hear someone who'll come out plainly on the side of postmarital sex.' A third declared, 'That's the kind of straight speaking those long-haired kids need up in Yorkville.' A fourth avowed that the chaos in Laos had suddenly been made clear to him.

My telephone rang all next day with demands that I speak to audiences, or take part in radio panels, or be interviewed on C.B.C. television. To be famous, I suddenly realized, one had to be incomprehensible. I'd intended to fire my secretary but instead kept her on. I also hired people who spoke such languages as Urdu, Etruscan, and Tamil.

My next speech, given to the Montreal Chamber of Comics, consisted entirely of little-known polysyllabics chosen at random from the English dictionary, and interlarded with gross obscenities in Turkish, Aramaic and Australian. For greater effect, I read it backwards. Yes, they lapped it up, afterwards telling me, 'We need mighty intellects like yours in these difficult times when apathy and indifference are running amok.'

Requests came pouring in for me to write a book, accept a university presidency, serve as communications consultant to huge industrial companies. One Conservative senator asked me if I would stand ready to take over in 1979. Everywhere, my name was on people's lips – 'Did you hear what McGargle said about sibling-oriented ochlocracy?' or 'I think there's a lot in McGargle's theory that the exponential is antithetical to the schismatic.'

I had everything going for me till once more my secretary stabbed me in the back. After a lunch-break spent entirely at the bar, she typed out the speech I was to make that evening before the Daughters of the

Vampire. As I stood up to give my address, my eyes fell with horror on the opening words: 'Once upon a time there were four little rabbits; and their names were Flopsy, Mopsy, Cottontail, and Peter. They lived with their mother in a sand bank, underneath the root of a very big fir tree.'

I went right through with it to the end, 'But Flopsy and Mopsy and Cottontail had bread and milk and blackberries for supper.' There was perfunctory applause, interspersed with yawns and hisses. I stole from the room, a ruined man. So here I am now, with my beak in the beaker, and wondering what's to become of me. Antinomian, collegiality, holistic, ontological, – say, do you think I could get a job making the announcements over the loudspeaker system at Toronto International Airport?

Judge, that ye be not judged

Pardon me, sir (said the man at the bar) but you badly need a haircut, and your clothes look as though they've been slept in, and the way you toss back your drinks indicates you are well on the road to becoming an alcoholic.

A rude approach, you think? Indeed, and there's a reason for it, which I'll explain. But first let me offer you some Canadian Club, a drink which brings out our basic national characteristics. After one ounce, you say, 'There are obvious difficulties'; after two, you inquire, 'Where's the money coming from?'; after three, you cry, 'Whatever it is, it can't be done!' and then sink into a catatonic trance.

And now to my story. I was brought up in the customary fashion, with everybody constantly telling me that I had done the wrong thing, or that I had said the wrong thing, or indeed that I was the wrong thing. My father would say, 'Why aren't you out playing hockey like normal, decent kids instead of sitting around all the time with your nose stuck in a book?', at which I would go out and play hockey. On my return, my mother would say, 'If only you read a good book occasionally, instead of pushing a stupid piece of rubber around the ice, you might do better at school.'

My teachers played the same game. One would say on my report card, 'Jamie daydreams all the time, and will not settle down to routine'; and another, 'Jamie is a plodder, who lacks imagination.' If I acted politely with teachers, the other students denounced me for apple-polishing, and if I acted impolitely with teachers, I got a tongue-lashing from the vice-principal.

In adult life, I found things no different. Friends, relatives and employers were forever giving me spiels which began, 'The trouble with you is that –' and continued for as long as five hours. They dinned into me my mistakes, my faults, and the grievous ways in which I had let them down, or hurt their feelings, or in some cases ruined their lives. My response was to apologize and humbly promise them I would try to improve my ways.

I lived thus for many years, until I made a discovery as remarkable as those of Archimedes and Newton. The world, I saw, was divided into two classes of people, those who criticize and those who are criticized – the judges and the judged. The judges, I perceived, were in no way superior to the judged; and the judged were in no way inferior to the judges. The simple fact of the situation was that some people took it as their right to judge; and others took it as their duty to submit to judgment.

At this point, sir, I decided that having been judged all my life, I would now do some judging myself. To make it easy, I started with a high-school girl, whom I noticed staggering along with 187 textbooks on top of her structured hairdo. Going up to her, I declared, 'You are a rotten little trollop! You have broken your mother's heart and driven your father to drink! You have failed in fiscal education, are failing in English decomposition, and will fail in political silence.' As the books tumbled off her head, she burst into tears and thanked me for helping her see the light.

To a boy student, I cried, 'All you ever think of is your own selfish pleasures; you never think of my selfish pleasures. What excuse have you for such incorrigible irresponsibility?' He started to shake, and handed over his transistor radio in a pitiful effort to placate me.

Gaining confidence in my career of judgment, I heckled, chastised and excoriated all with whom I came in contact. I scourged them for attitudinizing, dichotomy and procrastination. I accused them of buying *Playboy* for the articles, squeezing toothpaste tubes in the middle, and having no visible means of rapport. I charged them with cachinnation, impunctuality and reading the *Encyclopaedia Britannica* in the bathroom. All were grateful, saying, 'He tells us these things for our own good.'

All went well, sir, until today, when I found a man sitting on a bench in Queen's Park, serenely sucking on a bottle of gin. I lit into him for a solid half-hour, giving him 187 reasons why he was utterly worthless and irresponsible, following which he smiled beatifically, then repaid the compliment in masterly fashion. He charged me with having started the Great Fire of London, caused the San Francisco earthquake, invited the Mongols to visit Eastern Europe, and drafted the Ontario Liquor Control Act. He went on from there with a recitation of my crimes and follies that lasted several hours, and in a pyrotechnical conclusion claimed that I had cursed the world with such horrors as lump sugar, pedestrian crosswalks, vending-machine coffee, and the TV commercial.

So here I am at this bar, trying to restore my shattered nerves. It's as Captain Ahab asked, 'Who's to doom when the judge himself is dragged before the court?' Those were awful things he said to me, sir, but one of them hurt especially. Did he really have to accuse me of inventing the Christmas family reunion?

The sinner and the saint

nce upon a time, and in a thriving cosmopolitan city named Toronto-a-go-go, there lived a sinner and a saint. The saint's name was Howard Halo, the sinner's was Ferdinand Forktail, and they lived in the Wellesley-Yonge district where curvaceous young men wearing tight, tight pants stroll hand in hand with each other.

Howard Halo was saintly indeed. He was always praying and fasting and toting around books like Jeremy Taylor's *Holy Living and Holy Dying*. He was always mortifying himself by drinking Murray's coffee and reading newspaper editorials and attending obsessions of City Council. He was always blessing everything and everybody in sight. He went to Queen's Park each morning in his sackcloth robe and blessed the squirrels, who didn't appreciate it much. As one squirrel remarked, 'Some people bring us peanuts, and some bring us Humpty Dumpty potato chips, but all we ever get out of him is a cruddy blessing.'

The saint gave much of his money to the poor, who promptly proceeded to spend it on gin. He gave much of his money to university students, who, having obtained $50 from him to help pay their tuition fees, hared off to use the money as down payment on an MGB.

So virtuous was this holy man that the other Torontonians viewed him with bleak suspicion. They would say, 'He probably owns a string of slum properties where the cockroaches are so big that they scare the hell out of the rats.' Or they would say, 'He seems to get quite a charge out of blessing teeny-boppers.' Or they would say, 'That sackcloth robe would certainly come in handy for shoplifting.'

Ferdinand Forktail was, of course, quite the opposite. He had started his life of sin in a small-time way – derailing commuter trains, dynamit-

60

ing old people's homes, and ramming his yellow submarine into Island ferries packed with women and children. From these petty beginnings, he had risen in time to become a full-course sinner, who committed such monstrosities as being in possession of sweepstake tickets, selling flowers on Sunday and drinking beer in High Park. Since he had 187 mistresses, he hired a secretary to keep them all sorted out, and this of course made 188.

For all Ferdinand Forktail's depravity, people tried to feel sympathy for him. One would say, 'I understand he only went as far as Grade 12 in school, so what chance did he ever really have?' And another, 'His parents were quiet, respectable people, very devoted to each other. What kind of kid can you expect from an intact home?'

Now it happened one day that Howard Halo was in Allan Gardens blessing the begonias when a young lady approached him saying, 'Kind sir, may I offer you certain joys more to be imagined than described? My special price today is $17.50 plus 5 per cent Ontario sales tax.' The holy man naturally refused her offer, but pressed a $10 bill on the unfortunate waif, saying, 'Here, my child, buy yourself a nourishing meal and a pair of fishnet stockings,' at which point the Morality Squad appeared and arrested them both. When people heard about it, they said, 'You see? I was right about him all along!' and the newspapers had a big headline – Sex Maniac Nabbed; Deserves Lash, Says Magistrate.

At the same time, Ferdinand Forktail was lurching along Wellesley Street when he noticed smoke coming out of an apartment house inhabited by one of his 188 mistresses. 'Oh bad heavens,' he thought. 'Hildegarde does a nice job of ironing my shirts, and she stirs up a pretty good Wienerschnitzel, and she always has a bottle of King George IV Scotch around the place, and I haven't yet separated her from her life savings,' so he rushed into the building crying, 'Fire, fire!' When people heard about it, they said, 'You see, there was good stuff in him after all,' and the newspapers had a big headline – Hero Saves Hundreds From Blaze; Awarded Canada Medal.

Howard Halo is now in jail, where he spends his time calculating how many Anglo-Saxon Protestants can be accommodated on the head of a pin. Ferdinand Forktail is immensely popular and respected. He takes speaking dates with service clubs all over Ontario, and shudders only slightly when the waitress puts before him a plate of chicken croquettes with white sauce, green peas and boiled carrots.

The phantom of the airport

Every city worthy of the name has a subway, a symphony orchestra, a serious crime problem, a critical welfare problem, a desperate housing problem, an opulent public school system, an impoverished public library system, and an international airport where planes are constantly arriving from Frustralia, Fluoristan and Palestrina.

At such an airport twenty-seven businessmen, whose plane leaves for Montreal in ten minutes, stand foaming at the mouth and cursing in Fortran as a little old lady at the head of the line discusses the practicality of purchasing a ticket to Shrunken Head, N.B., for her daughter's twenty-seventh wedding anniversary next January. At such an airport, the television screens announce that your plane will leave from Gate 60, and the public address system that it will leave from Gate 40, while in point of fact it has just left from Gate 20.

In such an airport the announcement system cries by day and by night: 'Mr. Bonaparte, Mr. Napoleon Bonaparte, your economy ticket from Moscow to Paris is now available at the Aeroflot counter . . . Passengers will please remain satiated until the scarecraft has come to a complete flop at the infernal building . . . Mr. Eulenspiegel, Mr. Till Eulenspiegel, kindly cease and desist from your merry pranks and report to the K.L.M. counter . . . Ladies and gentlemen, women and men, wives and husbands, Captain Icarus is expecting some turpitude on our descent into Winnipeg; please fasten your chastity belts and make sure your squarebacks are in the uptight position . . . Beastly Airlines direct flight from Miami to Toronto has been slightly delayed at Havana, and will be arriving a week from next Tuesday . . . Mene, mene, tekel upharsin, which means, being interpreted, that you have been wait-listed in the Balearics and found wanton . . . We hope you have enjoyed your fright, it's been a pleasure having you bored . . . God help the Queen.'

We thus come to a particular airport, where an odd turn of events once took place. Over a period of time, the passengers, stewardesses and clerks noticed a strange-looking man with a long beard, who prowled around the building at all hours of the day and night. Some people said, 'Poor devil, he's probably been here for weeks, trying to remember where he parked his car.' Others said, 'He's an optimistic type who still entertains hopes that the baggage he checked through in Sudbury will eventually be forwarded from Istanbul.'

At the same time as the phantom made his appearance at the airport, the airline clerks noticed that their schedules kept disappearing, which was very awkward when someone inquired about flying from Buenos Aires to Paris by way of Prince Rupert. They finally called in the famous detective, Elementary Watson, who said, 'Have there been any strange people lurking about?', to which the airline workers replied:

'Most of the people who come here are normal, but they all get strange after waiting 35 minutes in the line-up, especially when they find out it's the wrong one. Perhaps the strangest of all is Rasputin J. Novgorod, who as every Air Canada employee knows, has 37 wives and 164 children under 12, many of them six feet tall. On the other hand, there has been this character with the long beard, who wanders around muttering to himself.'

Watson nodded. 'And what does he mutter about?' A stewardess volunteered, 'I heard him last night; he was mumbling something or other about Iberia still flying DC-3s, and Ethiopia serving a snack Thursday morning between Karachi and Addis Ababa, and how if you went by Finnair you'd probably end up at Jyvaskyla, which is nothing more nor less than you deserve in the first place.'

Using his mighty brain power, Watson said, 'As I piece all these difficult clues together, it becomes obvious to me that your phantom is a schedule addict. We must seek him out and give him the help he needs.' That evening, they tracked the mysterious stranger to a storage room in the basement of the airport, where they found him surrounded by times and tariffs from Allegheny to El Al, and from Lebanese International to Lufthansa.

The phantom weepingly explained, 'I've never ever been on an airplane, so the next best thing I can do is to read the schedules, watch them take off, and wonder how it feels to be six miles above Yoohoo, B.C., gnawing on the left leg of a defunct turkey.' The airline workers looked at each other, and had an idea, and took up a collection to give the phantom his first flight. So much money was raised that they were able to put him on a plane to London, and as he stepped off the Viscount at Crumbling Airport he drew a rousing cheer from the U.W.O. students.

Repent, the end is at hand

Men often get angry at God, and God sometimes gets angry at men, as for example when they fail to appreciate the fascinating world they live in. There was one such occasion when He looked down upon a city called Toronto, and thought, 'What a bunch of creeps! They have all sorts of food and drink and raiment, and comfortable homes to live in, and beautiful women to look at, and interesting things to do, instead of which they mope around looking like death warmed over. I think they are in line for a storm of fire and brimstone, which will destroy them utterly.'

St. Peter said, 'Quite right. You can't turn them into pillars of salt, because that seems to have happened with most of them already. But perhaps we should give them some kind of warning so they'll have time to straighten out their crummy affairs before they get fricasseed.' God agreed, and sent for a prophet named Isaiah Isotope, and dispatched him to Toronto with orders to tell everybody the jig was up.

Isaiah began his mission by standing at the corner of Bloor and Bay crying, 'Fire and Brimstone!', but the Torontonians didn't respond very well. They said, 'Fire and Brimstone? Isn't that the new rock group which is taking over from The Cream?' Or they said, 'I've often heard of a fire sale, but this is the first time I've seen it peddled right on the street. I wonder what sort of container it comes in, and if it sells by the pound, quart, foot, cord or bushel.'

Isaiah then made signs reading, 'Repent, the end is at hand,' and 'Where will you spend eternity?' and 'You have one week left to live.' The Torontonians were still unimpressed, saying, 'It is probably some kind of publicity gimmick which will end up with the gala opening of a self-service funeral home in Henpeck Heights'; or else they said, 'Those car dealers are absolutely shameless, and will stop at nothing to unload their old models.'

Isaiah saw he would have to break through their skepticism, so he performed a few miracles such as turning *Globe and Mail* coffee into coffee, and clearing lower Yonge Street of illegally parked cars, and making all the T.T.C. escalators function. The Torontonians then believed him, and realized they had only a few days to go.

Even at that, their response puzzled the prophet. One man said, 'Hurrah! First of all I will go up to my boss and let him have it right in the ugly. Then I will take all my money out of the pension fund. Then I will get magnificently stoned and stay that way until the fire and brimstone arrive.' A woman said, 'This is great good news. If you're going to die, why diet? I will dump my calorie counter and wash down an enormous plate of ravioli with two bottles of Valpolicella. Old Angelo's, here I come!'

A downtown businessman declared, 'There's a certain redhead at our office who is always waving her false eyelashes at me, but I have never spoken to her in case the fellows would think I was queer. Now the end is at hand, I don't care. I will walk right up to her, and ask her out to lunch at the North Toronto bus depot.' A housewife said, 'I will go to Eaton's and buy everything in their damn store and charge it, and then I will do the same thing at Simpsons, and then I will die happy.'

Another woman said, 'I have three men chasing after me, decisions, decisions. But since I'm about to be fried, the decision is delightfully obvious; and when I repent, I'll have something really worth repenting, hi-de-ho.' A high-school student said nothing at all, but smiled blissfully as he dropped his notebooks and texts one by one into the harbour.

With the end at hand, the Torontonians were suddenly happy. They sang in the bars, danced in the streets and even smiled at one another on the subway. So loud was their laughter and song that it reached as far as Heaven, where God sent for St. Peter, saying 'They are enjoying life so much that I've had a change of heart and won't broil them after all. Bring that prophet Isaiah Isotope back, or is he too busy piling up a fortune at the track? Oh yes, and put a full-page advertisement in the Toronto papers saying the Day of Judgment has been called off on account of rain.'

Thus, the city was spared. As the news got around, people went back to their schools and offices and husbands and wives, and life resumed its customary pattern. It would be pleasant to record that the Torontonians learned something from their narrow escape; but in fact they didn't, as you can tell from the way they mope around looking like death warmed over.

You can't manage without an M.A.

Bienvenue à Montréal (said the man at the bar of the Windsor Hotel) and permit me to guess that you are from Toronto. How can I tell? By your air of gloom and anxiety, by the way you tip an exact 10 per cent down to the last penny, and by the fact you've been eyeing that brunette for the last half-hour without having the courage to speak to her.

Cheer up, mon vieux, and let me treat you to a drop of Crown Royal, a regal distillation of which it's said that after one ounce you feel like King Henry VIII; after two, you feel like Mackenzie King; after three, you feel like King C. Gillette; and after four, you feel like King Kong, at which it might be wise to stop.

As you sip it, I'll tell you how I, a man of energy and enthusiasm, failed disastrously in the business world, and am now compelled to eke out a humble living by teaching elementary French to people who have graduated in that subject from Ontario universities.

It all began when I read the help-wanted section in one of the Montreal papers. One advertisement was for a waitress: 'The woman we are seeking will have at least a B.A. degree, and preferably an M.S.W. She will speak Russian, Japanese and Australian, and combine a working knowledge of differential calculus with a mastery of medieval Turkish literature.' Another was for a pants presser: 'The man we are seeking will have doctorates from McGill, Harvard, the Sorbonne, and Lakehead. He will be familiar with the later poems of William Wordsworth, have a firm grasp of Tasmanian mythology, and be able to translate the Bhagavadgita into Eskimo.'

Suddenly my eye fell upon an advertisement placed by a trucking company named Wilder Transports. They wanted a driver for the Quebec-Rimouski run. 'The man we are seeking will have an M.A. degree, and will have published at least three scholarly works in Arabic. He will be familiar with data processing systems, and be able to conduct seminars on Maori architecture. He must be an expert on Pushkin, Thomism, scrimshaw, Aristotelian metaphysics, and the sex life of high school vice-principals. He will be between twenty-five and thirty, and have at least fifteen years' working experience.'

Reading the advertisement, I realized that I had none of the qualifications. I went to Wilder Transports anyhow, and joined a huge mob of applicants, many of whom had come from as far away as Dalhousie and Simon Fraser. Telling lie after lie as I filled out the 187-page questionnaire (I said I'd got my M.A. at the University of Ulan Bator), I succeeded in winning the job, and was put to work driving a truckload of doughnuts along the rugged shores of the St. Lawrence.

By hard work and imagination, I moved steadily up with the firm, at last becoming its president. I reorganized Wilder Transports, competed ferociously with ships, planes and trains, and gradually built it up to become the biggest and most successful firm of its kind in La Belle Province. It made so much money, in fact, that politicians came down from Ottawa to remonstrate with me – 'Please don't pay us so much in taxes, we're running out of ways to blow it.'

All the time, sir, my conscience gnawed at me; I could never forget how I'd lied about having my M.A.; so I made generous donations to universities all over Canada. Thus came my downfall. One of them decided to grant me an honorary degree, did the customary research into my background, and discovered that dear old Ulan Bator had never heard of me.

The ugly news spread to my board of directors, who fired me immediately, declaring: 'Energy and enthusiasm and loyalty and ability and courage and integrity are all very well, but they can never make up for the lack of an M.A. degree' – an interesting comment considering the fact that most of them left school at Grade 10 and at least two had to sign their names with an 'X'.

I regretfully left the office where I'd spent twenty hours out of the twenty-four, seven days of the week, and now you see me here in the Windsor Hotel resting up between sessions with French professors from Ontario. They're a little shattering, I must say. 'Noo neerongs plews oaks boys, less lawyers song koopaze.' Merde!

And what happened to Wilder Transports? There was an announcement in the paper about them just this morning. They've gone bankrupt, and 1,500 truck drivers are now out of work. Do you suppose, sir, that Toronto could offer employment to 200 B.A.s, 300 M.A.s, and 1,000 Ph.Ds?

HOME AND SCHOOL

Crime and punishment

nce upon a time, there was a country whose federal authorities confined their activity to the deportation of industrious Greeks. In this country, there was a province whose politicians hid under the bed at the mention of wine, women, or weed. In this province, there was a city where instead of burying the dead, people elected them to high municipal office. And in this city there was a high school named Jugglemarks C.I., where you might have found a student named Roman Raskolnikov.

Raskolnikov was an agreeable young man who did well in such subjects as elementary mumbling, intermediate profanity and advanced cheating, thus preparing himself for a successful career in the business world or the political world or the academic world or indeed any other world. One day, however, he committed a terrible act in the history classroom. When the teacher, Mr. Forcepump Feedback, read out loud from the textbook that Jacques Cartier reached Canada in 1934, Raskolnikov shot up his hand. 'Sir, shouldn't that be 1534?' The teacher turned purple with rage, the students green with alarm and embarrassment.

Mr. Feedback cried, 'Do you mean to tell me, young man, that you have the insolence to question the holy sacred truth as contained in the holy sacred textbook?' – at which all the students reverently bowed their heads in worship; all save Raskolnikov, who stood his ground. 'Perhaps, sir, it is a misprint.' Mr. Feedback was furious. 'Raskolnikov, you will report immediately to the office of the vice-principal, Mr. Oliver Cramwell, and tell him of your unspeakable conduct. May Almighty God have mercy upon your soul.'

After Raskolnikov had confessed his vile deed, Mr. Cramwell played with the model guillotine which he used to sharpen pencils. Then he said, 'We at Jugglemarks C.I. have always prided ourselves on turning out a product – male or female, as the case may be – that will be acceptable to the personnel managers of Pow Chemical or the Glum Life or the Natural Bust. What will happen if word gets about that we have students so irresponsible' – at which he frowned and Raskolnikov shuddered – 'as to question the Holy Word promulgated by the Department of Education? There is a hard bench outside my office on which you will sit every day from 7 a.m. to 9 a.m. and from 3.30 p.m. to 5 p.m., thus bringing upon yourself the sneers, jeers and general contumely of decent, responsible students who are working toward Ontario dullardships.'

Reacting with anger at what he deemed a cruel punishment, Raskolnikov wandered along to the boys' washroom, where – finding himself alone – he pulled out a black crayon and wrote with it on the wall, 'The vice-principal is a fink.' Having done so, he returned to his classroom. The next day, Jugglemarks C.I. was in a dreadful uproar. The school authorities had offered a generous reward for anybody identifying the miscreant – a hand-woven copy of *The Modern Age*. The halls teemed with policemen in and out of uniform. Questions were asked in Parliament, and the bureaucrats in the Departure of Education were so upset they had only four martinis for lunch.

Raskolnikov wondered if he should confess, but decided against it, and went through his twice-daily detention. One evening, as he walked down Yonge Street, he saw an attractive young lady smiling at male passersby and trying to engage them in conversation. 'Who are you?' he asked, 'and how have you fallen to this life of shame?'

She replied, 'My name is Sonia Samovar, and I used to attend Madame Tussaud C.I. here in Toronto. But on my eighteenth birthday, I decided to take the afternoon off and purchase a recording of Sgt. Pepper's Homely Tarts Club Band or maybe Ludy Beethoven and the Moonlighters. I told the school it was for a dental appointment, they phoned my home to check up on me and, well, you know the rest of the story. I can never go back.'

The young man nodded. 'But do you have to do this?' Sonia answered, 'It is not so bad as it looks. Most men who pick up girls on the street are really looking for someone to whom they can tell their troubles – that their wives don't understand them or, what is worse, do.

When a man responds to my alluring glances, I steer him down to the
Honey Dew, get coffee for us both, and settle in to listen, cluck
sympathetically, and occasionally pat his hand. For the first half-hour, I
charge $5, for the second $10, and so on up the scale, with a 10-per-
cent surcharge for those who insist on showing me colour pictures of their
children taken on the Antique Carrousel at Expo 67.'

Raskolnikov decided to reveal his own terrible secret to her, and her
eyes widened as his grisly tale unfolded. She told him, 'You must turn
yourself in to the police and tell them it was you who did it. Perhaps, if
you confess, you'll be let off with a merciful sentence such as having to
read the collected speeches of Tommy Stanfield, Pierre Douglas and
Robert Trudeau. Perhaps they will let you pay off your debt to society
by drinking Carleton University coffee, or by being deported to Freder-
icton, where you will work at hard labour in the Lord Beaverbrook Memorial Car Wash, Shoeshine Parlour and Quick Lunch.'

Raskolnikov shook his head, saying, 'They will have to come and get
me,' at which Sonia seized his hand and led him to the office of an
immense newspaper called the *Mop and Pail*. 'Somewhere in this
impenetrable bungle,' she told Raskolnikov, 'is a gentleman of advanced
years named Rasputin J. Novgorod, who dishes out worthless advice to
all and Sundridge. Perhaps he can persuade you to confess your heinous
deed.'

As they entered the old man's office, he was snarling and cackling at
his secretary, Luscious Lindy, who paid no attention but continued to
paint flowers on her earlobes. 'Atheism is the opiate of the people. One
man's Mede is another man's Persian. Can a wet nurse find happiness
with a dry cleaner? Vice is its own reward. That microskirt makes you
look like a refugee from Canada Packers. What's this ugly talk of
Quebec breaking away from France? Santa is an acidhead. Gad, sir,
now that family allowances have been introduced, you'll see an end to
poverty in our fair land of Canada.'

As Sonia hovered anxiously at the door, Raskolnikov made his
entrance and blurted out, 'I have committed a terrible crime.' Novgorod
chuckled, 'Don't tell me, let me guess. You look to me like a high-
school student. Perhaps you made a pass at one of the women teachers.
Don't worry over it, my boy, she will cherish the golden moment in her
memory for as long as she lives. Perhaps you were caught reading
poetry when you should have been studying algebraic equations; that's
how I spent most of my own time in school. Perhaps you knocked off

two little old ladies with an axe; well, that's one approach to the world population problem.'

'It was worse than that,' said Raskolnikov, and told him the story. The old man blenched, and lit a fresh cigarette from one of the five smouldering on the edge of his desk. 'There's no hope or help for it, young man, you will simply have to turn yourself in and ask for clemency. Perhaps they will let you off with four years of Flop and Swill at the University of Toronto or that popular new course, Creative Rioting.'

Raskolnikov walked to the nearest police station, where he told the desk sergeant, 'It was I who wrote that sign on the wall at Jugglemarks C.I.' The sergeant made him repeat it, then cried out an order. Policemen came rushing from all sides, and in no time at all Raskolnikov was on his way to the cells. 'Keep up your courage,' cried Sonia, 'I will bring you food parcels containing such delicacies as Arctic charwoman, peasant-under-glass, Danish wastrels, and Bonanza cream pie.'

After a brief trial, the court announced its sentence, eight years in Etobicoke, at which Sonia let out a piercing scream and fainted. The judge continued, 'You will wear a grey flannel soup at all times, shave twice a day, and keep your chastity belt fastened until the plane comes to a complete flop at the interminable building. You will refrain from walking in the park, parking in the walk, dancing in the dark, singing in the rain, or walking your baby back home on a leash longer than six feet. Once a year, you will be allowed to have a bath at a temperature of 78.1 degrees.'

Sonia told him afterwards, 'The eight years will go fast, and I will be faithful to you in my own fashion.' So they did, and so she was, and now they are happy together in Toronto. With their high-school background, they have built up a prosperous little business faking notes for unscrupulous students, such as, 'Dere Mr. Procrustes: The reason Lucrezia didn't kum to skule yesterday is becus she wuz atacked by a grisly bear, thanking you, Mrs. Borgia.''

What I want is a husband

nce upon a time when dogs ate bones, and in a city that used its main traffic arteries as parking lots, there was a girl named Ellen Eggroll who had a terrible problem. At the advanced age of seventeen she wasn't even going steady, let alone engaged, let alone married.

Ellen's mother listened in on her telephone calls, but unfortunately, all of them were from other girls. Ellen's mother steamed open every letter addressed to her daughter, but never found anything more important inside than a bill for the insurance on her contact lenses. Ellen's mother said to her, 'Your complexion is a mess, and you hunch your shoulders, and your eyes are too close together, and your nose is too big, but outside of that I think some man should find you attractive, even if he was just a dirty magazine distributor, I mean him, not the magazine.'

Ellen herself was alarmed as girls even younger than herself snagged a guy and settled down to arid life in Plastic Place. As she saw her chances of holy headlock slip away, she pondered over the alternatives, thinking, 'I could enter a religious order, I suppose, but unfortunately I believe in God. The other sisters would laugh at me, and ask me if I just got off the Ark, and if I adhered to other outworn superstitions such as sin and salvation, and if I hid myself in the can to read the Bible.'

Ellen thought, 'I could become a librarian, I suppose, but I just don't have the legs for it, let alone the bazoom. They say even Raquel Welch wouldn't stand a chance at the Downtown Public Library here in T.O.' Ellen thought, 'I could become a school teacher, I suppose, but unfortunately I believe in education, and think it desirable that the young should be brought up to appreciate the classics of art and music and literature. I fear I will end up in one of those Yonge Street joints, letting happily married men smear paint on my poor little bottom.'

One day Ellen stood in front of the mirror, saying, 'I am miserable, I am desperate, I have got to the point where I would marry a coathanger if it asked me.' To her astonishment, she heard a metallic little voice saying, 'I will marry you, Ellen. I am a coathanger named Randolph Rack. I am a bit twisted on top, and hung-up on a number of things, but I have a wiry frame, I catch on fast, I rub shoulders with many important people, and I could easily get hooked on you.'

Ellen squealed with delight, and ran to tell her mother that she was getting married, to which Mrs. Eggroll responded by leaping several feet into the air, clicking her heels together, and crying 'Glory, hallelujah!' Coming down, she planted kisses all over her daughter, then rushed to the phone to break the great good news to all their friends and relatives. Halfway through she turned round, saying, 'Just who is it you're marrying, Ellen?' When Ellen replied, 'A coathanger,' Mrs. Eggroll nodded her head and said, 'Well at least a coathanger is good for something, which is more than I could ever say of your father or of mine, either. He will never be unfaithful to you, and will always stay home and not waste the family budget on poker and ponies.'

Ellen went to their minister and said, 'I would like to get married,' to which he replied, 'I would like to get divorced; oh well, we all have problems; where's the unlucky man?' Ellen said, 'I have brought him with me,' which made the minister look around in bewilderment. She explained, 'He is in my handbag.' The minister said, 'Poor fellow, he must have been on one of those quick-loss diets, all the water you can drink and a raw turnip every second Tuesday.'

Ellen said, 'Well, you see, er, he is a coathanger. Is that all right?' The minister sighed, 'Why, of course, a girl will marry anything these days. Just last week I married a girl to an alarm clock. With this ring I thee wed, heh heh. Next week I am marrying a girl to an electric eel, which even I think a bit shocking.'

Ellen Eggroll became Mrs. Randolph Rack at a beautiful service in St. Herod's United Church, and they afterwards took a house on Lemming Lane, with her going out to work and him staying home. Ellen enjoyed this for a while but one evening she came home in a bad temper and said to him, 'I work in an office all day, I work in the kitchen all evening, and you do nothing but hang around the place.'

Blowing her stack, she grabbed Randolph, bent him all up and threw him viciously on the floor, after which he suddenly turned into a strikingly handsome young man with waved hair, who spoke to her thus and as follows:

'Thank you *so* much, Ellen my dear, for breaking the spell cast upon me by that *reptilian* old witch. It's such a *gorgeous* relief to get out of those *ghastly* cupboards and that positively *sick-making* smell of perspiration. I must now arrange a *divine* party to mark my liberation, and would you mind *dreadfully* if I borrowed some of your clothes?'

Ellen looked at him, and then she burst into tears and fled, and what happened to her after that I don't know, though someone told me that she staggered off the train at Salzburg, crying 'Take me to your lieder.'

St. George and the Dragon

nce upon a time, and in Toronto of all places, there was a young man named George St. George, whose mission in life was to rescue maidens from dragons. He did this so valiantly that pretty soon there was a shortage of dragons; and since the young ladies concerned expressed their gratitude to him as best they could, there was also a shortage of maidens.

This naturally plunged George St. George into a state of gloom – Othello with his occupation gone. Wandering sadly about a suburban park one day, he found three teen-age girls who were simultaneously eating potato chips, chewing bubble gum, smoking cigarettes, drinking

Seven-Up, listening to blasts of gibberish from a transistor radio and reading a battered copy of *Playboy*.

As he eyed them, the oldest girl remarked, 'What the hell are you staring at, mister? Are you one of those dirty old men who gets arrested at the Exhibition for exhibitionism?', to which St. George replied, 'I am not a dirty old man, but a clean young one who is looking for maidens.' The oldest girl said, 'We can qualify for that, but don't blame us. It's just that the boys around here are so square and creepy, ecchh,' and she let loose a string of oaths far worse than the knight had ever heard in the thick of battle. 'Very well, then,' he said, 'now tell me, are any of you maidens being annoyed by a dragon?'

The biggest of the sisters (for such they were) promptly replied, 'You can damn well say that again. All three of us are being not merely annoyed, but bloody well persecuted by a horrible dragon named Diana, who lives just around the corner. She is old, fat, ugly and mean; she spends her whole life bugging the hell out of us, and calling us names and torturing us, and breathing smoke and fire at us, especially when she has been to a cocktail party.'

Securing the address of this repulsive creature, St. George donned his heaviest suit of armour, procured his longest and sharpest lance, mounted his sturdiest steed, memorized his hospital and medical insurance numbers, and set forth thinking to himself, 'My strength is as the strength of ten because my heart is pure, though unfortunately I cannot say the same about the rest of me.'

St. George had expected to find the dragon dwelling in a bone-strewn cave, and was mildly surprised when he found the address he had been given was that of a comfortable bungalow. 'My, my,' he thought, 'even the dragons have joined the affluent society,' and then, with his lance poised to thrust, rapped loudly at the door. To his further surprise, it was opened by a rather attractive lady of perhaps thirty-five. Seeing the knight, she said, 'It's too late, I just finished doing the laundry.'

St. George replied, 'What's this laundry bit? I am looking for a dragon.' The lady said, 'We don't have any dragons around here. You should try among the house mothers at the universities, or the head nurses at the hospitals, or the supervisors at the telephone company.' St. George said, 'But I have it on good information that this place is occupied by a dragon who is keeping three innocent and beautiful maidens in a state of captivity and harassment.'

The woman smiled wanly. 'Would the dragon's name perchance be

Diana? If so, I am he, she or it – Diana Dogberry, left a widow, alas, when my husband got clobbered by a fright elevator, and stuck with the upbringing of three girls who are aging me at the rate of one month every weekday and six months every Saturday, Sunday and statutory holiday.' As she spoke, St. George glanced past her into the livingroom, where he recognized the three girls he had encountered in the park. They were crouched in front of the TV set with filthy bare feet and broken toenails, watching a little old lady being knocked about by three Russian secret agents, and yelling, 'Hit her again, she's still breathing!'

St. George said, 'There is Moore Park to this than meets the Island. For all I know, you may be a genuine fire-breathing dragon who has cunningly transmogrified himself into the human form.' At this point, their conversation was rudely interrupted by screams and shrieks from the living room – 'Hey, Marm, when's dinner going to be ready?' and 'Marm, why don't we have colour TV like everyone else?' and 'Marm, did you wash my blue jeans?' and 'Hey, Marm, the cat's just been sick on the chesterfield; come and clean it up, the stink's killing me.'

Mrs. Dogberry said to St. George, 'So I'm the dragon around here, huh? I tell you what, Mr. Lancelot or Galahad or whoever you are, come and live with us for a while and find out for yourself. But don't bring your trusty steed in here; we already have one cat, two dogs, four goldfish, and six hamsters, all of which they pleaded with me to buy, promising they'd feed and look after them. So who feeds and looks after them? Right. We also have a turtle which they hide in my bed when I persecute them by asking them to close doors quietly, or to pick up their clothes off the floor, or to stop snitching cigarettes, change and subway tokens from my purse.'

The three sisters put on a virtuoso performance when their mother had company for dinner. One of them would belch loudly, then say in an affected voice, 'Oh, excuse *me*,' and they would spend the rest of the meal snickering. When Mrs. Dogberry proudly produced her Quiche Lorraine, one of her daughters would say, 'Did you cook that? It smells more like you dug it up from the cemetery.' They would kick and jostle each other under the table until one of them yelped with pain and knocked her glass of grape juice all over the white cloth.

Mrs. Dogberry's guests praised the food, but the children left most of it on their plates, because they had been gorging on hot dogs and Eskimo pies and root beer at a horrid little lunch counter near by. If she said to them quietly, 'The children in Asia would be glad of that,' the girls would answer. 'So why don't you wrap it up and mail it to them?' And if, after that, Mrs. Dogberry told them to leave the table, they would stomp off muttering that she was too uptight to take a joke.

But the Dogberry girls were really at their best when some man showed up who admired their mother. Giving her no affection themselves, they bitterly resented the idea that she should get it from someone else. So when Mrs. Dogberry had a masculine visitor, the girls referred to him behind his back (and not always behind his back) as Horseface or Tomatonose or Big Blubber or Gold Fang or Grandpa Moses or Daddy Shortlegs or Gordon the Boredom.

They would say in front of him, 'Hey, Marm, why aren't you wearing your glasses? You know you're blind as a bat without them,' or 'Hey, Marm, you left your falsies in the bathtub,' or 'I'm so tired, Marm, you kept me awake all last night with your snoring,' or 'Hey, Marm, what's that Second Debut guck you've been using?' or 'Marm, there's a dead cockroach in the john.'

St. George noticed that the girls made telephone calls lasting as long as four hours; and when their mother protested, said, 'Everyone else on the block has two phones, and the Harris kids each have one of their own. Why do we have to live like peasants?' He noticed that any opinion expressed by Mrs. Dogberry was deemed by her children to be wrong, stupid, and dating back to the Ice Age.

He noticed that they never raised a finger to help her with the housework; that they fought with each other like wildcats; and when they'd finally reduced her to tears, would yell 'Take to the hills, the dam has bust!' and scurry off to the nearest horror movie.

The knight finally grasped the situation after a battle in which the mother said to the oldest daughter, 'I'm sure Harry is a nice enough boy, but I don't think he's quite the right one for you,' to which the girl screamed back, 'Just because he has long hair, wears temple bells, drops acid, and has been busted five times, you're prejudiced against him! I suppose it will be Jews and Negroes next!'

St. George told Mrs. Dogberry, 'I now see that you are not the dragon at all; it is they who are the ravaging beasts around here.' Mrs. Dogberry replied, 'I'm glad you have realized the fact. But who's going to do what about it?' He said, 'I have a scheme to rest you and to reform them. I will tell the children that I am taking you away to punish you for the terrible things that you do to them – like turning off the TV set at 1 a.m. and holding down their allowances to $5 a week, and expecting them to eat breakfast in the morning. You and I will then go to Montreal, where I will pursue dragons at Terre des Homards, while you pick out Mod dresses at Dupuis Frères. Once you're gone, the girls will realize how much they need you.'

After Mrs. Dogberry had consented, St. George told the three teenagers that he was taking their mother away for punishment, and she would be gone a week. One said, 'Only a week? Why not a month?' Another said, 'Sock it to her, George baby, make her howl for mercy.' The third said, 'Why don't you just slay her, like you do the other dragons? An old bag of 35 is no good for anything any more.' St. George thought, 'When she's gone, you will change your tune,' and then he and Mrs. Dogberry flew off to Montreal.

After she'd been absent a few days, Mrs. Dogberry started to worry about the children, and decided to telephone home. The line was busy on the first 187 attempts, but then she got through and spoke to her oldest daughter, saying, 'Doreen, this is your mother,' to which Doreen answered, 'Yeah, I know, wadda ya want?' Mrs. Dogberry said, 'I just wanted to know if everything was all right,' to which Doreen answered, 'I guess so.' Mrs. Dogberry said, 'Has anybody been asking for me?' and then heard Doreen yell at the other two girls, 'Hey, you guys, it's her. She wants to know if anybody's been asking for her,' and they yelled 'Nah,' and Doreen told Mrs. Dogberry, 'Nah. When ya coming back? Ya buy anything for us?' Mrs. Dogberry said, 'What would you like me to buy?' and Doreen said, 'I dunno,' then hung up.

When Mrs. Dogberry related this conversation to St. George, he said, 'So she wanted to know when you were coming back. That's very significant. It shows they miss you. But don't return immediately; stay a couple more days, and let the lesson sink in. You mark my words, Diana, you will see tremendous changes from here on. They will treat you with respect and affection, and will always be putting their arms around you, and telling you what a wonderful mother you are. They will vie each other for the honour of washing the dishes and taking out the garbage and cleaning up after the dogs and walking to the drug store to buy you ciggypoos.'

St. George grew enthusiastic. 'I can just see it all. Instead of watching TV or hanging around the shopping plaza, they will go for long, healthy walks in the country and bring you back bouquets of wild flowers picked with their own little hands. They will take paper routes and part-time jobs at the A. and P. They will make their own clothes, and read the *Book of Knowledge* you got them, and peddle Christmas cards for UNICEF, and visit little old ladies in hospital. They will enroll in Sunday school and join the Girl Guides and learn how to boil an egg and sew on a button. Everybody will say how fortunate you are to have three such lovely daughters, and there will be an article about you in the woman's *Globe and Mail* under the heading, "Happiness Is a Thing Called Home Life".'

St. George flew back to Toronto with Mrs. Dogberry, and they took the limousine to her home. When they got there, they found twenty-five motorcycles outside it labelled Beelzebub's Bunch, and thirty-three labelled Lucifer's Legion. There were also four police cruisers, two paddy-wagons, an ambulance and a fire-truck. The lawn was littered with empty beer bottles, and half the windows in the house were smashed. A police officer asked Mrs. Dogberry, 'Are you the mother?' and when she nodded, said, 'It must have been quite a party. Come along to the station, and you can make arrangements about bailing them out.'

Mrs. Dogberry smiled sadly and got in the cruiser, leaving St. George where he stood. The knight thought for a while, and then went to procure his steed and lance. 'Perhaps,' he thought, 'I would do better to go and wrest the Holy Land from the grip of those accursed Saracens.' He rode off to the Crusades, and is riding there still; everybody admires his courage and faith, and nobody has the heart to tell him about Moshe Dayan.

Mary had a little lamb

nce upon a time there was a suburb named Limbo Lane, and in it there was a school named Spoonfeed Secondary, and in it there were 1,500 students being brainwashed, manipulated and generally processed to spend the rest of their lives working in the glue factory.

To attain this noble end, the young ladies and gentlemen immersed themselves in such subjects as stultification, vulgar factions and long derision; elementary cotton-picking, intermediate finger-painting and advanced sandbox; quadratic equitation and French irregular blurbs. They drew maps of Miami Beach, Waikiki Beach and Mahlon Beach. They studied the War of the Noses, the Thirty Beers War and the Boxcar Rebellion. They answered examination questions which went thus and as follows:

(1) Sacking cities was Genghis Khan's bag. Comment. (2) Translate into Sanskrit, Swahili, Elvish and Desperanto this famous German saying, 'Vive la différence!' (3) Draw a map showing the location of the following – Outer Darkness, Tutti Frutti, B.C., Peyton Place, Farrago, N.D., Yes, Virginia, and the United Airlines Republic. (4) Compare in twelve words or less two outstanding literary works. *Hamlet* and *Nurse Jane Goes to Moose Jaw,* under these headings – plot, characterization, and the number of semi-colons in each book. (5) Write a fifty-word précis of Einstein's theory of relativity. Marks will be deducted for use of profane language. (6) Rasputin J. Novgorod has 187 mothers, all of them young enough to be his daughters. Explain this to the management of the *Mop and Pail.* Explain it also to Air Canada.

The principal of Spoonfeed Secondary was named Michael Mammon, and he was always issuing proclamations over the public address system. One day, he convulsed the school by announcing, 'Now hear this, you filthy little swine. The Board of Education just had a meeting at the Raffles Hotel in Singapore, and decided we should devote one full day to sex education. Since the single teachers know little about the subject, and the married ones even less, every teacher will have to use his or her own lousy judgment. Keep the faith, baby!'

There was one young teacher in the school named Cuthbert Covercourse who had original ideas. He told his class, 'The best way to learn about sex is from birds, bees and other small animals, which probably don't get much kick out of it anyhow. You must each bring a small animal to school tomorrow.' Accordingly, one student brought a tarantula, another an oyster, another an amoeba, another a streptococcus, another a rattlesnake. One student brought a bird, which went straight for Mr. Covercourse's eyes; another brought a bee, which buzzed up the teacher's pant-leg, causing him to leap through the air like Rudolf Nureyev.

Only one student disobeyed the instruction to show up with a small animal: this was a foolish and headstrong girl named Mary Metrecal, who arrived leading a lamb. The janitors and teachers were furious when they saw her come in. An English teacher said, 'You ain't got no right bringing that there animal into this here school.' A French teacher inquired, 'Poorquoy avaze-vouse broughtay oon agno dong set aycoal?' A biology teacher said, 'Where did you get that giraffe, Mary?' The janitors all cried, 'Time and a half for overtime,' and the lamb cried, 'Bah!'

Word of Mary's evil deed soon reached the Board of Education, which by now was assembled at the Maria Isabella in Mexico City. They wired Mr. Mammon, 'Unanimously agree expulsion only answer.' Mr. Mammon wired back, 'Don't quite dig, expel Mary or expel lamb?' The trustees wired him again, 'Expel Mary, you clod; lamb may have makings of Ontario Scholar.'

Mary was duly expelled from Spoonfeed Secondary, and forced to eke out a living teaching English to immigrants who had just arrived from Australia. The tarantula mysteriously wound up in a room labelled 'Staff Women', while someone gave the rattlesnake a warm home in the pocket of the vice-principal's overcoat. The amoeba was fruitful and multiplied, and now fills the whole cafetorium. The streptococcus felled all the janitors; and the oyster was eaten by Mr. Covercourse, who subsequently perished and went to Heaven, where he was welcomed by a gentle female voice saying, 'Hi theah, Whitey.'

The lamb became an excellent student, the kind which school administrators cherish. It's agreed around dear old Spoonfeed that he is well-behaved, quiet and co-operative, though he sometimes acts a bit sheepish. They had him speak at an assembly the other day; it is true he just went 'Bah!' into the microphone and walked off, but the students and teachers said that of all the speeches they had ever heard at an assembly, his was far and away the best, and the Board of Education sent a highly complimentary telegram from the Mark Hopkins in San Francisco.

The family that stays together

Not all children turn out badly; some turn out disastrously, and this was the experience of a middle-class couple who might once have lived in Toronto, and might have been named Marvin and Marcia Marmalade. More by accident than by design, they had engendered three children, who were sweet enough when small but on reaching their teens had developed into veritable monsters.

The oldest of the three was Attila, 21, who worked at casual jobs and belonged to a motorcycle gang named Hitler's Heroes. His naked chest was tattooed with naked females, threatening slogans such as 'Hell can't hold me,' and outright obscenities. He wore his studded motorcycle boots to bed and wouldn't take them off even when he had his annual bath. He lived mainly on beer, and filled the refrigerator with so many cans of it that there was scarcely any room for food. In the saddle-bags of his Harley-Davidson were a bicycle chain, a set of brass knuckles and the head of a defunct chicken. He hardly ever spoke to his parents, and then only in snarls.

Lucrezia, 19, was a hippie who idolized Timothy Leary, Allen Ginsberg and the Grateful Dead. She subscribed to underground papers which bristled with four-letter words, and insisted on reading them out loud to her parents at the breakfast table. She had long straight hair, which she ironed one day and curled into an Afro the next. She took off her shoes on May 1, put them back on November 1, and never washed her feet in between. She burned incense all over the house, wrote poems which consisted of the same word repeated 187 times, and screamed 'Pigs' every time a police car went past. She hardly ever spoke to her parents, and then only in grunts.

Caliban, 17, was enrolled at Dick and Jane Memorial C. I., but only showed up there when he was out of pot and had to get a new supply from the Grade 12 pusher. He headed an acid-rock group called the Warsaw Convention, and brought them over every evening for four-hour rehearsals, amplified to the point where every house in the block trembled on its foundations. When there was company present, he showed up in the living room wearing African tribal robes, with his hair in a ponytail and smoking a six-foot-long waterpipe. He hardly ever spoke to his parents, and then only in mumbles.

Marvin and Marcia Marmalade were held closely together by their mutual detestation of their offspring. He would say, 'It must be the awful curse of the Marmalades. We could ask or even tell them to leave, but they wouldn't; they are much too comfortable here. The family that stays together, preys together,' to which she would answer, 'Perhaps they will be with us until we die; I would settle for just one year of peace and quiet before I go to meet my Maker.' She would say, 'Perhaps we should simply pack our bags and steal away, leaving the whole place to them,' to which he would answer, 'This place is the only place we've got, and it's almost paid for, and I don't feel like giving up everything I've worked for these twenty-five years.'

One day Mr. Marmalade came home with a look of great happiness on his face. He told his wife, 'I have a plan,' and when he spelled it out to her, she clapped her hands with joy and mixed two martinis to celebrate. The next evening, Lucrezia stormed in and slammed the door and rushed to the telephone, only to discover it wasn't there. She screamed at her mother, 'Where the hell is the bloody phone? Did you move it some damn place?' Mrs. Marmalade quietly answered, 'Your father is having some business troubles, and we must economize, so the telephone has been taken out.'

Lucrezia let loose a string of block-busting oaths, as did her brothers when they heard the news. The next evening, the television set was gone, with Mrs. Marmalade telling the children, 'The bank is pressing your father very hard; I don't know if we can even hang onto the house.' Subsequent evenings saw the disappearance of the hi-fi, the car and the refrigerator.

Mrs. Marmalade had usually spread a good table, but as time went on the roasts of beef were replaced by hamburger, then by macaroni, then by stale bread spread with margarine and peanut butter. In the end, Mrs. Marmalade told her trio, 'We will have to give up this house and take a much smaller one. Instead of having your own rooms, you will all be in one, with a sheet hung across the corner for Lucrezia.'

With that, the three children disappeared, never to be heard from again, though Mr. Marmalade thought he saw Lucrezia's picture in the paper one time; she was leading a massed charge of hippies against the American Embassy, to protest the Russian occupation of Czechoslovakia. The Marmalades settled down to watch Merv Griffin and listen to their records of the Mormon Tabernacle Choir; but without the constant menace of their children to hold them together, they gradually drifted apart; and the latest one hears is that she got an uncontested divorce from him on the grounds of hypochondria, narcissism and skinny-dipping.

Alice in Examinationland

nce upon a time, there was a suburb named Acrimony Acres, and in it there lived a young lady named Alice Aforethought. She was very attractive, but had one awful fault; she was curious, and was especially curious to know what would happen if she took a generous gulp from her father's bottle of Scotch. One day, when both her parents were out, she did just that, and promptly passed out in a dream which had her falling, falling down a long, dark shaft until she landed on the bottom with a thump.

Standing around her were a strange group of creatures – a White Hobbit, who was always looking anxiously at his watch; a Mad Satyr, who kept staring at her and slavering in an impolite fashion; a March Square wearing three-buckle galoshes; a Persian lamb cap; and a badge which read, 'Help Stamp Out Yorkville'.

In a ladylike way, Alice asked, 'Where the hell am I?', to which the March Square replied, 'You are now in Examinationland. What was the surface temperature of Lake Inferior on May 17, 1912?' Alice shook her head. 'I haven't the vaguest idea. And in any event, who cares?'

At this, all the animals closed in on her, screaming, 'You're a failure, a failure! You're ignorant, uneducated, anti-social, irresponsible, uncooperative, a misfit, a freak-out! You won't be able to get a good job!' Alice said sharply, 'I don't want a job, good or bad. I just want to marry a rich man considerably older than myself, who will indulge my expensive tastes and allow me to have all sorts of lovers. But what's with this Lake Inferior bit?'

Stepping forward, the White Hobbit said, 'Here, let me do the Tolkien. We people in Examinationland work on a simple system. If you know the surface temperature of Lake Inferior on May 17, 1912, you are educated. You will probably win an Ontario dollarship and go to university and become a Bachelor of Tarts, or perhaps a Doctor of Philanthropy, all of which will assure you a good job on the dissembly line at the Bored plant in Chokeville. If, on the other hand, you do not know the surface temperature of Lake Inferior on May 17, 1912, you are no good, you are a flop, and will end up like one of those welfare mothers, raising seventeen children in a steamer trunk.'

The Mad Satyr seized Alice's hand and started chewing it all the way up to the elbow, meanwhile remarking: 'You really are a delectable creature. If x equals the Holy Roman Empire, and y equals the square root beer of 187, how about coming with me to a discreet little motel what I wot of near Watford? Has anyone told you your skin tastes like chocolate ice cream? Give the definition of a definition. Don't you think older men are more tender, more considerate? Discuss the relationship between the War of the Squamish Succession and the rise in Baffinland's banana production. How about it, baby?'

After Alice had shaken him off, the March Square started heckling her with a barrage of questions. 'Why did the southern fried chicanery cross the road? Define: Demonetization, badness, it, Sylvanus Apps, CHUM, 1970, Rumpelstiltskin. State the essential difference between a man and a woman. Following this, report immediately to The Office. A man shouts across a cave, and the echo comes back three times. What did he shout? Name the person who sneezed in the middle of Churchill's most famous speech. State how an amoeba's sex life differs from that of a vice-principal. What is the hypotenuse of a rhomboid? Translate the Lord's Prayer into Australian, omitting all references to God. The Canadian National Exhibition plans to meet the challenge of Terre des Hommes by starring Doris Day, Mackenzie King, Charlotte Whitton, Billy Graham, Count Dracula, Richard Nixon, Senator Platitude O'Dreary. Which of these is (1) correct (2) utterly disastrous? In the middle of a summer solstice, would you be better off with a syllogism, a solecism or a solipsism? What did Nero fiddle while Rome burned? Was he paid union scale?'

Alice stamped her foot and shook her fist at the animals, crying, 'This is just a lot of jabberwocky, balderdash and gobbledygook. You are only trying to confuse me!' They snarled with rage, and laid hands upon her, and dragged her off to a long, flat building which might have been a factory or a hospital or a penitentiary, but in fact was boldly marked Colesnotes Secondrate School. 'To the examination room!' they cried, and hustled her through a bleak maze of corridors to an enormous hall where students sat crouched over desks, trying to figure out the connection between the Battle of Blenheim and the 1929 stock market crash.

Waving his arm, the March Square cried: 'A noble spectacle! Today's paper was drawn up by Malaysian head-hunters and will be marked by African pygmies who do not speak or write any language, including their own. The students who fail will be taken directly to the Scott Mission. The students who pass will be given work-permits entitling them to punch a time-clock at the C.N.R. fright yards for the next thirty-five years; those who score high marks will be allowed to enter university, where their elephantine memories will enable them to add 187,000 worthless facts to the 187,000 they packed in at high school. Quick, Alice, tell me a fact.'

Alice said, 'You are all crazy, and that's a fact.' The March Square frowned. 'It can't be a fact, because it isn't in the textbook. Only in the textbook are the factual facts to be found, such as that' – and he quickly produced and opened a textbook – 'such as that the capital of Italy is Peru. Or that the population of China is 234,579. Or that Iceland is the world's chief producer of orchids.'

'But none of those things is true,' said Alice. 'They must be misprints or blunders. Maybe the man who published the book was drunk, and maybe the author was, too.' The Mad Satyr intervened. 'Be that as it may,' he said, 'They are in the book, and therefore will be on the paper, and therefore must be true. Come to Montreal with me, ma petite poupée, and we'll stay at that new C.P.R. hotel, the Chateau Cheesegrater. Why did Vergil write the Aeneid in Latin? Answer yes or no.'

The White Hobbit got into the act, saying to Alice: 'What are you trying to do? Make a nuisance of yourself? What will your dear old parents say when the school informs them that you are a dirty, rotten little failure? How do you think you're going to manage in this world without a degree? Even the Barcelona bus drivers read Plato in the original Arabic. Now sit down and write the examination.' Alice stared in wonderment at the piece of paper he thrust into her hands:

(1) Is atheism a threat to organized bingo?

(2) 'The mediocrity is the message.' Translate and comment.

(3) Identify and state the historical importance of the following: (a) Queen Elizabeth I having black teeth; (b) Puritans eating turkey at

Thanksgiving instead of corned beef; (c) Shakespeare's hair style; (d) none of the above.

(4) Compose a sentence using the words 'hypothecation' and 'sex,' and explain why you used those two words.

(5) If $x(2 \times 3y \times 24z) - 184 \times 2(4 \times 19c \times 43e) \times IOU$ equals 13, why is this not true? Steps taken to solve this problem must be clearly shown on your paper.

(6) In Act VI, Scene III, Line 84, of *King Lear*, the author uses the word 'damn'. In not more than 14,000 words, describe your reaction on reading this.

(7) From the meanings offered below for each of the capitalized words, choose the meaning you think is correct: AND – also, in addition to, aussi, hand, pickle; SCHOOL – place of learning, institute, prison, home, hell; CHOCOLATE – fat, hat, pimple, dimple, supercalifragilistic expialidocious.

(8) Translate into Greek – (a) I would like to see the Eiffel Tower, please. (b) Are the Beatles playing in the Coliseum tonight? (c) How much does one normally tip a charioteer? (d) Please pass the waitress. (e) Richard Needham is still at large in Athens. Help!

Alice studied the paper carefully. She then reached into her purse, took out a cigarette and lit up. With the rest of the match, she set fire to the examination paper and watched it vanish in smoke. Following her lead, the students all did the same thing, the whole building vanished in smoke, and Alice found herself back on earth.

She tried to tell her parents what had happened; but having heard her lie for a solid eighteen years, they refused to believe her. Alice accordingly went downtown and saw an aged newspaper columnist, who cackled with glee as she told her story. He promised to print it, patted her hand, and told her that if she laid off the booze and the coffin-nails, she might some day be as much of a decoration to Toronto as Linde Hurkens.

A sound of deviltry by night

In the city, you can go broke on $10,000 a year; but in the suburbs, you can do it on $15,000. Suburbanites accomplish this in some measure by staging lavish cocktail parties at which matrons gobble pizza as they discuss their weight problem, and men get smashed out of their skulls while they boast how they gave up smoking.

What function these parties serve (outside of plunging the host and hostess further into debt) has long baffled sociologists. My theory – true for myself, at least – is that the cocktail party is a form of shock treatment comparable to the snake pit of earlier times. So great is the horror of it, so keen the sense of relief at escaping, that all one's other sufferings and problems are reduced to triviality.

Finding myself beset by fortune's slings and arrows not long ago, I subjected myself to the ordeal by guzzle, gabble and gorge at a home so far north of the city that several of the guests greeted each other by rubbing noses. The usual cocktail-party types were on hand – languid immigrants, inferior decorators, insulting engineers, gloomy dames, misplaced trustees, impractical nurses, a dean of women who had been fired for having men in her room at all hours of the day and night, a marriage counsellor who announced that his third wife had just left him for the fifth time, and a psychiatrist who kept getting down on his hands and knees and frisking about the place, nipping at the women's heels.

It is customary at these gatherings to have the phonograph on at full blast; this forces people to shout and scream at each other, which in turn dries out their throats, which in turn causes them to get bagged more quickly, which is why they went to the party in the first place. Having no opinions or information worth bellowing, I customarily listen to those of others. Standing near a group of women, I caught the following fragments:

'The only thing I have against men is me . . . *The Naked Ape* is disgusting, I stayed up all night reading it . . . I don't know how old she is exactly, but she does enjoy a nice hot cup of tea . . . Even a newspaperman is better than no man at all . . . We eventually had to leave Picton; the pace was too fast . . . I keep having this awful nightmare; a big brute of a man is chasing me, and I escape . . . I found out early on Bay Street that all men are married, but some are less married than others . . . I didn't mind Jack's cruelty and extravagance; what finished it off was the way he kept clearing his throat every five minutes.'

Going out in the garden, I found a young man who told me, 'I hate university but I have to stay there so I can graduate and get a good job, and pay back the money I borrowed to go to university.' The young woman with him said she had a different problem. 'It's my parents. They're so good and kind and trusting, and I'm so rotten. When I come home drunk at two in the morning with my clothes torn, and tell them I was in a car accident, they believe me. This makes me feel guilty, and so I become twice as rotten. I wish I had parents like Jill; her father drinks his pay, and her mother runs around with every man on the block, so she doesn't have to feel guilty about being even more rotten than I am.'

Going back into the house, I listened in on a group of men: 'I've always thought of Highway 7 as the square route . . . When the postal strike ends, how will people be able to tell? . . . I've at last figured it out, Doris Day is her own grandmother . . . I know beer's the drink of moderation, that's why I hate it . . . When your plane lands in Toronto, you have to set your watch back thirty years . . . Liquor at the C.N.E.? It's enough to make Judge Robb turn over in his grave . . . I'm still looking for a woman who measures down to my standards . . . I didn't mind Marge's boozing and infidelity; what drove me out was that she never changed the blade after shaving her legs with my razor.'

It seemed at this point I'd had enough, so I finished the Scotch-and-tonic someone had pressed on me, said farewell to the hostess, and made an inglorious exit by tripping over the dachshund. Still, I was safely out; I wouldn't need to do it again for a long time; and I walked steadily south until the crumbling tenements, polluted air, garbage-littered streets, and screams of hold-up victims informed me I was back in civilization.

NOW SERIOUSLY

All's square in shove and bore

An English judge once described marriage as a state of antagonistic co-operation, and it's been that way for many centuries, sometimes with the emphasis on the co-operation, sometimes with it on the antagonism. Socrates battled with Xanthippe 2,500 years ago, Abraham Lincoln dreaded going home to his Mary, and how's everything with you, dear reader – you in Applewood Acres, you in Don Mills?

Perhaps marriage isn't meant to bring happiness, any more than life or work are meant to be fields of bliss. Nature doesn't give a damn if people are happily married or not; all nature wants is for men and women to have children, as many and as early as possible. Hence the strength of the sexual drive.

I don't think the church cares that much whether people are happy or unhappy in their marriage; it just wants them to get married and stay that way; none of that there divorcing, none of that there living in sin. The Holy Almighty State doesn't give a damn whether people are happily married or not; it simply wants them to be married because that way they are forced to work and pay taxes and meekly obey its laws.

The business world has similar fish to fry; it wants people to be married (happily or unhappily, as the case may be) so it can sell them stuff, lend them money to buy homes, etc. Another reason it wants people to marry is so they'll toil more faithfully in the glue factory. From the employer's viewpoint, married workers are more 'reliable' than single ones – and less likely to fuss over honesty, integrity and similar folderols. Wasn't it Cavour who said that a married man would do anything for money?

Do parents, even, care if their children make happy or unhappy marriages? Most mothers pressure their daughters into early marriage – partly to get rid of them, partly in hopes of getting them to the altar before they manage to get themselves pregnant. I'm also inclined to suspect that an unhappily married woman gets a certain glum satisfaction (what the Germans call Schadenfreud) from having a daughter in the same boat.

Thus it goes, and probably will go. Some marriages are happy, some miserable, most of them (I suspect) just so-so, with each partner wishing occasionally at least that the other would disappear, not die necessarily – just somehow disappear. Isn't that one of the many, many reasons why war always has enjoyed, always will enjoy, a certain popularity among us humans? In setting forth to fight, he frees himself and her; and there's a chance he won't be back.

But that's going at it the hard way. William James said we should find a moral equivalent for war, in the sense that war enables men to be heroes; perhaps we also need a moral equivalent for war in the sense that war gets husbands and wives away from each other. I've often thought all marriages should be dissolved after twenty years, or perhaps when the youngest child is sixteen; the man and woman concerned can remarry each other, if they so wish.

If that's too drastic, we could heed Kahlil Gibran's advice, 'Let there be spaces in your togetherness,' or the advice of Freya Stark, 'Absence is one of the most useful ingredients of family life.' Many unhappy marriages would be a little less so if wives could have a day off, week off, month off, all to themselves. There might be sense in having a sabbatical, as the universities do – every seventh year off, every seventh year apart.

But here we come to an irony that's all too typically human. The happy, trusting marriage (yes, I know some of them) allows and indeed encourages frequent separations; the unhappy, suspicious one doesn't. So we end up right where we started, which is where one usually winds up in any discussion of marriage. The problem's insoluble; and maybe that's bad news for you – you out there in Don Mills, in Applewood Acres – but the lawyers downtown aren't complaining, and the psychiatrists look to their future with confidence.

Goodbye, dear high schools, goodbye

I won't give the name of the high school concerned; I'll just say it's one of Toronto's oldest and best-known, and once had a distinguished academic record. Roughly a month ago, a boy who attends it asked if I would come and speak to the students; I said, 'Sure,' set a date and honoured it.

After the meeting, a woman teacher came up and spoke pleasantly to me. In the course of the conversation, either she asked me or I volunteered (I don't recall which) to come there and gossip with her English class, this being a subject about which I know a little and with which I've had a little success. In any event she expressed enthusiasm, so I promised her that as soon as I got back to the office, I would drop a note setting a day and time. This promise, too, I honoured.

In response to my note, I got the following letter signed by the same teacher who had expressed pleasure at my agreeing to talk with her class: 'Dear Mr. Needham: This will acknowledge receipt of an inquiry from your office concerning the prospect of your visiting this school on June 2, 1969. I regret that I must inform you that your request cannot be granted.'

The letter was co-signed by the principal of the school; I presume he had drafted the mean, nasty little missive and forced her to sign it. Okay, I know the way it is; she had to knuckle under or else lose her job. But she could at least have phoned me or written me or dropped into the office to explain, perhaps apologize for, the turn of events. She didn't even have the courtesy, or perhaps I should say the courage, to do that.

This is by no means an isolated incident. I've been visiting high schools all across Canada for the past four years, and could tell dozens of stories along this line. It's as Edgar Z. Friedenberg says, the high school is an ungracious institution; it has very bad manners, which stem essentially from its anxiety and suspicion – frightened administrators, frightened teachers, above all, frightened students. The high school stinks of fear.

That's the chief reason why I won't be visiting high schools any more; I've been in about 250 of them now, and I know all I want or need to know about them, I know rather more than I want or need to know about them. On most of these visits I was accompanied by Luscious Lindy or Notorious Nancy or both; they're relieved that there won't be any more of them.

Lindy says she can't cope any longer with the boredom – bored students, bored teachers, bored administrators. Nancy says the high schools depress her. 'Each time I walk into one, it is with a sinking of the heart. The regimented, lock-step day (ring bell, take up books, shuffle to next class) is really too much for any human being's spirit. Teachers on the whole I find a timid, awkward, unimaginative lot. As for the students, all I can do is feel heartily sorry for them as they are processed to take their dull, grey places in a dull, grey society.'

Fear is death, boredom is death. When I go to a public school I expect to find – usually do find – vitality and enthusiasm among the students, curiosity, imagination, joy. I hardly ever find these things in the high schools. The students are sad, apathetic, unimaginative, cynical toward everything and everybody. Certainly, they are cynical toward education as I would understand it – the cultivation of the mind, the appreciation of what is noblest in human life and human accomplishment.

They are in school because the law says they have to be in it – or because their parents say they have to be in it. They are in the school to pass examinations so they will get their Grade 12 or 13. Then they will 'Get a good job'; or else they will go on to university; why? 'To get a good job.' The whole emphasis isn't on nourishing the mind, but on getting jobs and making money.

I suppose it's the parents rather than the teachers. In its interesting examination of the American high school (May 16, 1969) *Life* reports that while the majority of teachers think the primary duty of the high school is to produce students who ask questions, the majority of parents think its primary duty is to prepare them for jobs or for university, to control and discipline them. The high school is seen simply as an extension of the home.

But whether it's the parents or the teachers, the students or the administrators, I've had it. Accustomed as I am to horrors and disasters, I just can't take it any more – the sterile buildings, the jangling bells and God-like public announcements, the bitterness and anger, the stupefying boredom, the omnipresent fear. So good-bye, dear high schools, good-bye; I believe in life, I believe in love, I believe in learning, so from here on I will go where the life and the love and the learning are. They sure as hell aren't in the high school.

A question of loyalties

 ome forty or fifty years ago, England had a highly successful novelist and playwright named John Galsworthy. He wrote a play called *Loyalties*: it's about the theft of some money in one of those English country houses and the way in which various people reacted to it, each in terms of his own particular loyalty.

One man was loyal to his religion, another to his race. Another was loyal to his family reputation; another to his club, another to the army, another to the law. A woman was loyal to her husband; a man was loyal to his mistress.

In Galsworthy's play, one character says, 'Loyalty comes before everything', to which another replies, 'Well, yes, but loyalties cut up against each other sometimes.'

The young Canadians who have entered university this fall are finding out – or perhaps have found out already – that loyalties do have a way of cutting up against each other, getting in each other's way, forcing them to decide – as only they can – which loyalty they are going to put first.

Most of the class entering university this year have spent eight years in public school, and five years in high school. At these places, they were brainwashed and regimented into loyalty to a system of education which is certainly a system but is not, in my opinion, education. They were taken out of the world – the real world of actual people, places, situations – and put into horrible little boxes. They had bells ringing at them all the time, and disembodied voices screeching at them over the public address system in such languages as Urdu, Swahili and Australian.

They had to keep in line, be on time, obey the rules. Rather than ask questions, they had to accept the answers – the official answers – handed down to them from on high. Rather than learning to think for themselves, to learn for themselves, they had to memorize thousands of facts for the purpose of passing examinations – facts they forgot within a week after the examinations had been written, facts they will never need in life even if they do remember them. They were treated not as individual people – each with a heart and soul and personality of his or her own – but as things, to be regulated and controlled.

They were told, and they believed, and perhaps many of them still do believe, that getting an education means getting a piece of paper – the Grade 12 certificate, the Grade 13 certificate, the B.A. degree. They were told that this piece of paper would get them a job, or a well-paying job. Perhaps it will, although I know a great many people who have managed pretty well without.

But having a piece of paper doesn't mean they've been educated. Some of the best educated people I know had little in the way of formal schooling; and some of the stupidest people I know have enough scraps of academic paper to cover a wall. I believe strongly in education – the getting of knowledge and wisdom – I believe in it more strongly than anything else in the world – but I do not believe it's a matter of buildings or top-heavy administrative systems or horrid little bits of paper, so I'd suggest this is one loyalty a student should get rid of. The high-school nightmare is over; be done with it; take Dostoievsky's advice, and squeeze the slave out of yourself, one drop at a time.

Much has been said, much will be said, about loyalty to society, to the social and economic system which surrounds us. But just what is society? Is it the chambermaid at the Château Laurier? The bank manager on St. James Street? Is it the farmer in Saskatchewan, the fisherman in New Brunswick? These are all very different people with very different interests; so how can anyone be loyal to them? Canada is a nation of 21,000,000 people – 20,000,000 of whom we never have seen, we never will see.

But agreeing there is some sort of social and economic system in Canada, just why should one be loyal to it? What beauty or truth or integrity or wisdom does it offer? So far as I can see, the chief aim of our social system is that everyone should conform, everyone should be dull and passive and respectable, everyone should do the same things, and have the same possessions, as everybody else; that they should live the same life, by the same values, as everybody else. I really cannot regard this as a noble system; I really cannot regard the acceptance of it, let alone loyalty to it, as a manly objective.

As for our economic system, it appears to be based on two squalid and unmanly principles. One is that everybody should make a lot of money – you're a terrible failure if you don't – and the other is that everybody should be what is called, I believe, secure. In this matter of money, I'll agree that a person needs a certain amount of it to live on – but he doesn't need very much of it.

A person can only eat one meal at a time, wear one suit or dress at a time, sleep in one bed at a time, occupy one room at a time. The majority of people in Canada today do not have as much money as they want, but in my opinion they have a lot more than they need and that's their problem.

In any event, there are more important things to do than making money. I think it's better to pray or sing or make love or compose a poem or write someone a pleasant letter or pick some flowers and take them to a girl friend or just sit on a rock and think. Perhaps our cities would be better cities if people earned less and spent less, if they thought more and loved more.

As for security, I simply do not believe in it. In this world of change and struggle and revolution and war and death and disease and depression and inflation, I don't see how anybody can be secure. Furthermore, I don't see why anybody – any young person especially – should want to be secure. Do our young people really want everything to be the same, every day to be the same, for the rest of their lives? If so, they had better go down to the nearest funeral home and turn themselves in; they're dead already, and they need to be buried in nice, safe, secure little graves.

The class of 1973 has heard much, and will hear more, about loyalty to the state – meaning the Ontario Government, the Canadian Government, constituted authority in general. How loyal should a person be in that direction? Should a man meekly obey every one of the state's laws? Should a man meekly pay every one of the state's taxes? I was speaking the other day to some university students and I asked them three questions.

I asked first: 'Do you think there should be any limitation on the amount, the proportion, of your earnings which the state takes away in taxation?' They were silent.

I asked a second question: 'Do you think there should be any limitation on what the state can do with your body – putting you to forced labour, for example, or conscripting you for foreign wars?' Again, there was silence.

I asked a third question: 'Do you think the state has the right to enforce any laws it wishes regarding, let us say, sex or marriage or drinking or gambling; regarding a man's clothing or his work or his manner of life; regarding Greeks or Asians or Jews or Mennonites or any other minority group?' Still again, there was silence.

And I simply told them, 'You are slaves! You have no concept of individual privacy or liberty or dignity. The state could pass a law telling you to walk on your hands and you would do it; the state could pass a law sending you to the gas chambers and you would meekly take your place in line.'

Politicians are not God, the state is not God, the laws are not God, schools are not God, social and economic systems are not God. Only God is God. Everything else is human, it is therefore corrupt, it must therefore be placed and kept under continuous criticism, questioning, and, where necessary, defiance. That's what freedom is all about.

I have watched the operations of the state for a very long time – the British state, the Canadian state, the American state, the German state, the Russian and Chinese states. They are all much the same.

I have reached the same conclusions about the state which Thoreau and Gandhi reached before me – that it is a liar, a coward, a bully, a robber, a cheat, a mass murderer and a bungling fool. Belsen, Hiroshima, Coventry, Dresden – no individual man or woman would dare to affront God in this fashion. The state did, and does, and will continue to do so. Be careful, be very careful, with your loyalty to it.

The class of 1973 has heard much, and will hear much, about loyalty to the world. But it really is a very big world; at last count, there were almost four billion people in it. Where should a person start? How can we help the world? Are we really sure that it even wants to be helped? The great Spanish-American philosopher, George Santayana, observed the world at pretty close quarters through his long lifetime. He concluded that the world is not respectable; but is mortal, tormented, confused, deluded forever. He wrote:

'The world does not wish to be saved. If we say the world thereby wills its own damnation, we are merely venting our private displeasure, without frightening the world.'

I myself have reached the same conclusion as Santayana. I recently wrote in my notebooks, 'To understand the world, you must realize that it is only interested in fighting, fornicating, getting drunk and smashing things it just built.'

The class of 1973 has heard much, too much I rather suspect, about loyalty to parents. This is something about Canada which never ceases to astonish me – the way in which parents hang on to their children, try to possess them and dominate them and make them go this way or that, live this or that kind of life. As a parent of three grown children, I'm horrified by the way in which other parents extract emotional blackmail from their sons and daughters.

Boys of nineteen and even twenty tell me, 'I'd like to leave home but my mother would be terribly upset.' Girls of nineteen and twenty tell me, 'I'd like to spend the summer in Europe, but my father won't even hear of it.' My God, isn't this a free country? What's this slavery bit? I know, I know, the Bible says a person should honour his father and mother. I would take that to mean one should treat them with politeness, with respect and, if one can manage it, with love.

But surely it doesn't mean a person has to jump every time they crack the whip. Surely it doesn't mean a person has to fear them, to be frightened of upsetting them or annoying them or hurting their precious feelings. Let me say to the class of 1973 with all the force at my command: 'Fear is death. You should never fear anyone, you should never fear anything, in this world.'

So what's to be loyal to? I would say to the class of 1973 – be loyal to good men, if you can find them. Be loyal to great books, great

teachers and poets and philosophers, great ideas. Be loyal to gentleness
and tolerance and wisdom. Be loyal – if and as you find them – to
courage, honesty, dignity, integrity, responsibility, manliness. Be loyal to
love, laughter and beauty. Be loyal to faith, hope and charity. Be loyal
to God. He is not dead, but lives within you – in what there is that is
best within you.

Be a man. Be a woman. Be yourself. And this, above all, is the
loyalty I would recommend to you – the one which will never let you
down. Be loyal to yourself, your own heart, soul, talent, personality, the
principles you have developed, the wisdom you have acquired. Don't
ever be ashamed of being who you are, what you are; every one of you
is absolutely unique. Never in the history of this world has there been
anybody just like you; there isn't today; there never will be again. You have
your own life to live, live it. You have your own contribution to make,
make it. You have your own star to follow, follow it.

But be sure in every case that it is your own, that you are expressing
and developing as well as you can this unique personality you have been
given. For when it's all over, and you have to give an accounting, God
will not ask why you weren't Bob Dylan or Pierre Trudeau or Joan
Baez or Melina Mercouri. He will ask simply, 'Why were you not
yourself?'

TALES OF NOVGOROD

Samantha's sinister secret

nce upon a time, and in would you believe Toronto, there was a delightful young lady named Samantha Systems. She was well-groomed, attractive and amusing, in these respects being rivalled by many other girls in the great city.

In one respect, however, Samantha differed from them and indeed from everyone else. She was a machine, manufactured by the skilful people up at International Business Machines in Don Mills. During the daytime, Samantha worked as a shorthand-typist at the Brutal Life Assurance Company, where nobody, not even the personnel manager, knew her terrible secret. At night, she retired to her tidy little apartment in Topless Towers.

The I.B.M. people had prepared Samantha for all the needs and problems of a woman's life in the big, wicked city. They programmed into her 1,000 different ways to say 'No, no, 1,000 times no'; and 187 different ways to say, 'The matter will be taken under consideration'; and one way to say, 'Yes, I will, yes.' They programmed into her 38 ways to look helpless; 57 ways to cause problems requiring male assistance; and 95 ways to find out if the man who came to her aid was married.

They equipped her with mildly naughty stories to tell the men at her office, and with truly dreadful ones to tell the other girls. They built into her the ability to stand on the subway from Eglinton to King, with the seats all occupied by men hiding behind their copies of *The Globe and Mail*. They programmed her to be lonely and stay home much of the time, this being the fate of most attractive women in Toronto. They programmed her never, never to tell anyone that she was just a machine.

The only mistake the I.B.M. people made with Samantha was on the side of accuracy. They programmed her to answer all questions correctly, and this gravely damaged her prospects of romance; for as every woman knows, the average Canadian man enjoys nothing better than to tell a woman she is wrong about something, preferably in front of other people, and force her to admit she is ignorant and stupid.

But this mistake was soon remedied; the I.B.M. people reprogrammed Samantha so she would give wrong answers every now and again, thus causing men to feel superior to her, and so be willing to accept her company. After this, Samantha went out with the types known to every Toronto career girl.

She went out with men who wore elevated shoes; with men who used expressions like 'frinstance' and 'irregardless' and 'anti-climatic' and 'accidently'; with men who only took an amorous interest in her when they were too drunk to do anything about it. She went out with an English teacher who said, 'I seen' and 'I done'; with a French teacher who introduced himself to her as 'urn professewer der fronk-say'; with a history teacher who informed her, 'Where Napoleon made his big mistake was in firing Bismarck.'

She went out with a man who told her, 'If only you were a man, we could be good friends'; with a Mountie who was terrified of horses; with a man who said, 'Stop trying to fool me, kiddo. I know I'm not the first one'; with a man who told taxi drivers they had taken the long way around, and threatened to report them to the Metro Licensing Commission. She went out with men who knew all about the Electoral College and insisted on explaining it to her; with men who talked about money when they made love, with men who talked about politics when they made love, and with men who were grimly silent.

She went out with a man named John Smith who signed the motel register as Wolfgang Mozart, and with a man named Wolfgang Mozart who signed it as John Smith. She went out with a celebrated bachelor who at the moment of truth said he would appoint a Royal Commission to look into the matter. She went out with a man who demanded total fidelity from her, while he himself pursued half the miniskirts in Southern Ontario.

After years of this, Samantha thought to herself, 'I have absolutely had it, and am just about ready to go back to I.B.M., and ask them to disassemble me and make me into a cash register or a golf-ball typewriter or some damn thing. I will go to that cocktail party in the

Leeway Hotel tonight, and if I don't meet a half-decent man there, it is Endsville.'

To Samantha's curiosity, there was an interesting-looking man at the cocktail party; to her pleasure, he kept looking at her; and to her joy, he finally walked up to her saying, 'My name is Leopold Zoom, and I hope you will not take offense if I tell you that you are the most attractive woman in the room.' Samantha got him out of there quickly before any other woman could sink her filthy claws into him, and talked to him in the bar, and realized in short order that she had encountered that great rarity of our day and age, a first-class man.

Leopold Zoom was at once strong and gentle, masculine and considerate. He had manners that would have drawn attention in the House of Lords, and dressed in a style that would have impressed Harry Rosen. He spoke beautiful English, and was fluent in French, German and Spanish. He had a firm grasp of history and literature, told fascinating stories about far-away parts of the world, and did everything well, from fixing a leaky tap to ordering a full-course dinner at the Tiroler.

If Samantha was attracted to Leopold, he was no less attracted to her, and paid her many beautiful compliments. He told Samantha, 'The ambition of every rose is to look like you.' He asked her, 'How can anyone say God is dead when He brings such a beautiful creature as you into existence?' He told her, 'The sun rises in the morning so it can shine on you, and sets at night so the moon can have its turn.'

Can a machine fall in love with a human being? That's what happened to Samantha, who started feeling all sorts of strange and wonderful emotions. It seemed to her that the birds were warbling Waldteufel waltzes, and that the breezes were whispering Leopold's name in her ear, and that the stars up there in the sky were spelling it out. She smiled so much everywhere she went that all the men thought she must be a tart; while the women, realizing she was in love, glowered at her and reached for their stilettos and poison blow-guns.

Samantha started to daydream at work, imagining the office as a medieval dungeon and her boss as a wicked ogre, from whom Prince Leopold would rescue her with a noble flourish at noon and again at five. She absent-mindedly began business letters with 'My dearest darling' or 'Leopold my love,' and ended them with a row of capital X's. Responding to her obvious adoration, Leopold soon became even more first class than ever.

He kissed her passionately on crowded elevators. He had flowers delivered to her at the office by a Boy Scout bugle band. On rainy days, he'd quite literally pick her up at work; in front of the whole office staff, he carried her from the door to his car, so she wouldn't get her feet wet or her coat splashed. He would take her to a business lunch with three other men, and spend all of it holding her hand, lighting cigarettes for her and passing silly notes to her that made her laugh.

Leopold sent Samantha a love letter every day. He put a full-page advertisement in all three papers declaring her the most desirable woman in Toronto. He told her he would never buy her jewels because they would only mar her perfect beauty. He had an 8-foot by 10-foot enlargement made of her photograph and hung it on his office wall. He had announcements made over the P.A. system in restaurants, 'Paging Miss Systems, Miss Samantha Systems, you are wanted by Leopold Zoom.'

Only two things marred Samantha's happiness – the knowledge that she was a machine, and the fear that Leopold Zoom would find out. In this respect, she had several narrow escapes. One day, he took her to the races, saying, 'What a huge crowd!' to which she answered, 'Yes, 33,785,' causing him to look sharply at her. Another day, he asked her the time, and she answered without looking at her watch, 'It is now exactly 3 hours, 46 minutes and 27¼ seconds.' Another time, he told her, 'You're so neat and quick in your movements, I'd almost think you were a machine,' which caused a rabbit to scuttle all around her stomach.

As time went on, Samantha developed a third cause for concern – the look of sorrow which crossed Leopold's face even during their most blissful moments together. 'What is it?' she would ask, 'Have I done or said something wrong?' He would tenderly answer, 'You could never do or say anything wrong, Samantha; you're perfect for me in every way. It's just that – oh, forget it. I'll tell you about it some day,' but he never did.

Hell hath no fury like a woman's curiosity aroused, particularly when it involves the man she loves. Samantha pried and poked away at Leopold, but never found out what was on his mind until the night she got him sloshed on straight tequila, then demanded to know, 'What is bugging you, Leopold? You must tell me, or I will kill myself,' which of course she hadn't the slightest intention of doing.

Leopold stood up and put his hands on her shoulders and looked her straight in the face, saying, 'I have been deceiving you since the moment we met.' Samantha said, 'Oh, all men do that. Just tell me her name and address, and I'll have her knocked off by the Mafia.' 'No, no,' said Leopold. 'It is far worse than that. For God's sake, Samantha, forgive me for hiding it from you all this time. I am not a human being, but a machine, made by I.B.M.,' at which he burst into tears, and so did she.

Samantha's first impulse was to tell Leopold, 'It's all right, in fact it's wonderful. You see, I too am a machine made by I.B.M.' But then she thought to herself, 'How can I tell him that I've been misleading him all this time; allowing him to think I was a human being?' So as Leopold sniffled, she patted his hand and said with an air of great nobility that she forgave him for his deception. 'However,' she added, 'I must think about what we do next.'

Wandering away by herself, Samantha pondered. 'I could go down to the *Mop and Pail* and see dear old Rasputin J. Novgorod, but I understand he is busy with plans to wed Maria Callas and set up housekeeping on Ward's Island. Hmmm. I think I will seek advice from the queen of the Bay Street belles, Knavish Trixie, who is reputed to have wrecked half the homes in Mediocrity Meadows.'

Samantha found Trixie in a bar called the Harlots and Varlets and briefly stated her problem, at which Trixie blew a couple of smoke rings in the air, then said, 'Mendacity, evasion and concealment are necessary to survive in this world, especially for us poor downtrodden females. I myself told the truth only once in my life, and then I didn't hear the question properly. Now as I would see it, you can extricate yourself from all the lies you've been telling to Leopold with one final lie, a real whopper. Tell him there's a clinic in Copenhagen where they perform an operation that turns human beings into machines. Tell him you love him so much that you're going there to have the operation performed on you; and that when you come back a week later – no longer a human being, but a machine – you will marry him. You can spend that week hiding out in Montreal or some place.'

Samantha did exactly as Knavish Trixie had told her. Leopold Zoom swallowed the story completely, and was waiting at the airport when she returned from her alleged trip to Denmark to tell him that the operation had been a success. Leopold said, 'I am the happiest man of all 10,234,857 in Canada.' Samantha said, 'From now on, we will be together 86,400 seconds of the day.' Leopold said, 'If we get married tomorrow, our 25th anniversary will fall on a Tuesday, and our 50th on a Saturday.'

Yes, they got married in a delightful ceremony at the Sin-in-the-

Dark, the only untoward incident being when the minister said, 'I
hereby pronounce you, pronounce you, pronounce you,' going on until a
technician came racing over from I.B.M. and fixed him. Samantha and
Leopold now reside happily in Torpor Township, where they have three
little ones – a C.C.M. tricycle, a sewing machine and an electric hedge-
clipper.

The chicken coquette

ost girls are fortunate enough to have a father
and, especially, a mother. But in a Canadian city named Blunder Bay,
there was once a girl named Polly Puccipants who had no parents at all,
both having perished from the deadly venom of a windshield viper.

Everybody felt sorry for her, especially girls of her own age. 'Poor
Polly!' they would say. 'She has no father to telephone the police when
she is five minutes late coming home from a date, or to go and see the
principal about her report cards. She has no mother to tell her she is a
slob, and forbid her to wear false eyelashes and bikinis, and ask her if
the boy she is going out with has mentioned marriage yet.'

Polly told them, 'Now that my parents are gone, I will immediately
leave high school, as 99 per cent of girls would in similar circumstances.' Her friends said, 'What are you going to do then?' and she
replied, 'Well, I suppose I could become an impractical nurse or perhaps
a witchboard operator or perhaps a goof-reader on one of the papers,
but what I'd really like is to enter the world's oldest profession. I will
become a high-class bore, varlet or maul-girl.'

Her friends said, 'But whereabouts are you going to do this?' Polly answered, 'I have considered the matter carefully. The men in Newfoundland are very passionate but they don't have much money. The men in Victoria have plenty of money, but I fear are too old to take much interest in my utterly divine person. I shall therefore go to Toronto, where the men are both rich and passionate, and will soon have a penthouse apartment with a Japanese maid, a circular bed, a sunken bathtub, and oodles of poodles. Once I am successfully launched in my chosen career, you must all come and see me.'

Polly flew to Toronto, and went straight to the spot which has the most men with the most money – the corner of King and Bay. But here she ran into difficulties. She was shy, and could not bring herself to make a straightforward pitch. She smiled brightly at one well-dressed man, and said to him, 'I was wondering, well, like, that is . . .' and he looked at his wrist and said, 'It is just 10:27, and I know that's right because I always set it by the clock on the old City Hall.' She smiled brightly at another, and said, 'Pardon me for bothering you, sir, but I would just like to ask . . .' at which he said, 'Why, of course, there is one just down the hall from my office, and I will have my secretary take you there.' She smiled brightly at another, and said, 'You seem like a nice man so perhaps you would enjoy . . .' at which he said, 'Now really, miss, I must have spent a fortune on raffle tickets, and never win anything, so thanks, but no thanks.'

Polly's heart sank to her granny shoes as man after man got away from her. Finally, one of venerable years came up to her and said, 'How on earth did a young slut like you rise to this noble occupation?' Polly started sniffling, and told him her story, at which he cackled with glee and took her to lunch and said to her:

'You obviously aren't cut out to be a high-class trollop, or a low-class one, either. Besides, you are now in a community where the amateur competition is perhaps more intense than anywhere else in Canada, and where women have been known to give their all simply for a kind word. Why don't you come and help me write my memoirs, or would that be dragging you down too far?'

Polly consented, and between them they settled on a salary of $37.50 a week. Each day, the old man related some chapter of his life to her, causing her to blush in many interesting shades of red and pink, and to wonder why Providence – or some woman, or some husband, or some mother – had not hanged a millstone around his neck and drowned him in the depth of the sea.

'And did you love every one of them?' she asked, to which he replied,

'Oh yes, they were all first-class and utterly delightful. I loved Joan because she never washed the back of her neck, and Sally because she ate with both hands and feet, and Sonia because she told me lies which would put Baron Munchausen to shame, and Irmgard because she did her laundry by taking it into the bathtub with her, and Simone because she was unfaithful to me every day of the week and twice on Sundays, and Greta because she got into fistfights at cocktail parties, and Diana because at moments of high romance her stomach gurgled.'

Polly's friends came down from the Lakehead to see her, and asked, 'Where is the penthouse apartment? Where are the poodles and the Japanese maid?' She replied, 'I am sorry to tell you this, but I tried being a high-class bore, and failed with flying colours, and now I have been reduced to typing the memoirs of an aged man who, if he is telling the truth (which I gravely doubt), should be put in the Royal Ontario Museum on his demise, or indeed before it.'

They were horrified and said, 'Let us take you away from all this,' but she demurred. 'It is too late to save me. I am reasonably happy in my life of shame, and getting an education of sorts. Besides, we are right in the middle of the 188th chapter, and I have to find out if that librarian really did go up to the top of the new City Hall and drop the *Encyclopaedia Britannica* on him one volume at a time.'

A bad man is hard to find

 nce upon a time, and in the remote fishing village of Rum Cove, Nfld., there was a remarkable young man named Simon

Pure. The remarkable thing about him was his goodness; he was virtuous clear through, in all respects living up to his name.

When Simon grew up, his parents said to him: 'Your goodness is clearly a gift of Divine Providence, and you must make full use of it, which is difficult in a small place like this. Rather than hide your light under a Bushmill's, you should go to a big city like Toronto, and let it shine among men, women and school trustees.'

Simon asked, 'Speaking of women, what are they like in Toronto?' His father replied, 'From what I have heard, you should be popular with them, since they are every bit as virtuous as you are. They dress and behave modestly, faint on hearing an uncouth word, donate 10 per cent of their earnings to missionary societies, and expect a gentleman to ask permission before lighting a Turret, Virginia Oval, or Sweet Caporal in their presence.'

Simon accordingly went to Toronto, where he joined a church, taught Sunday school, fed the birds, directed little old ladies to the betting shop, distributed Alka-Seltzer at AA rallies, gave first aid to the injured at peace demonstrations and helped welfare recipients load their weekend supply of beer into their Thunderbirds. He didn't drink or smoke, but used the money instead to take underprivileged children to the Island, where they slaughtered every living thing in sight.

When it came to women, however, he fared poorly. Far from being the bashful violets depicted by his father, Simon found the women of Toronto to be noisy, profane, riddled with nicotine and alcohol, and as shameless in their attire as in their pursuit of men. Far from being attracted by Simon's rectitude, they were turned off by it, saying, 'He has an unwholesome flavour of goodness about him,' or 'There's one who writes his mother a seventeen-page letter every day,' or 'I suppose he gets his kicks by walking through the girdle section at Eaton's,' or 'So he goes to the Y each day to keep fit; fit for what, I should like to know,' or 'I know his disgusting underhanded type – a brisk healthful walk in High Park, followed by a chocolate ice-cream soda at some crummy lunch counter, ecchh.'

In the end, Simon got so lonely and depressed that people felt sorry for him. They told him, 'What you need is advice; and the easiest place to get it is from dear old Mr. Novgorod at the *Mop and Pail,* who enjoys the reputation of being a gregarious hermit, a harmless villain, a cynical idealist, a bibulous teetotaller, an honest charlatan, and a misogynist who positively dotes on women. Having made a spectacular ruin of his own life, he now spends his time telling other people how to correct and improve theirs.'

Making his way to the newspaper building, the hapless youth was directed to an office which grandiosely styled itself the Rasputin J. Novgorod Home for Lost Souls, Absent Minds, Mistaken Identities, Abandoned Women, Vanishing Adolescents, and Fallen Men.

As Simon entered, the old man was dictating to a blonde secretary who paid no attention whatsoever, but continued to read Gore Vidal's *Myra Breckinridge* with her eyes popping out of her head. Novgorod ranted away, 'The capital of Iceland is Buenos Aires. The four angles of a triangle total 187 degrees. Wordsworth's *Idylls of the King* wasn't written by Bacon, but by Shakespeare,' at which Simon boldly asked, 'Pray, sir, what is the meaning of this meaningless farrago?'

The patriarch genially answered, 'Why, these are incorrect facts, as against correct ones. The trouble with our world today is that its leaders are guided by correct facts, the result being endless wars, strikes, inflation, depressions and similar misfortunes. With a store of incorrect facts at their disposal, such as Napoleon defeating Hannibal on the Plains of Abraham in 1867, our rulers could not do worse and might perhaps do better. This is how I am helping them, and how can I help you?'

The young man stated his plight, and received the following advice: 'Your problem is a matter of timing. In the old days of Toronto, people presented the outward appearance of virtue, that being what made them acceptable. Now things have changed about. In Toronto today you become acceptable by presenting the outward appearance of vice. If you are hoping to impress Torontonians, and particularly those who belong to the more adventurous sex, you must have an air of wickedness about you – something that will arouse every woman's curiosity, and cause many of them to think they can reform you.'

Simon objected that he neither wanted nor needed reformation, to which Novgorod readily agreed. 'Still, if you're going to interest women, you must have an aura of evil – nothing unpleasant like murder, of course, though I'm told murderers are inundated with offers of love and marriage – but something which combines a reasonable amount of safety with a reasonable amount of mystery and excitement. I tell you what I will do. I will put it about the business area that you have been divorced three times, owe money all over town, have a serious drinking problem, and are under analysis.'

Novgorod spread the word around King and Bay, and as a result women began looking at Simon Pure with that speculative eye which causes any experienced man to race to Toronto International Airport and grab the next flight for Kuala Lumpur. They started sitting next to Simon at restaurants, and introducing themselves to him, and looking furtively to see if his hand shook when he lifted his coffee cup, and asking (in a casual, detached sort of way) what he thought about marriage, and lending him books by Erich Fromm, and sliding thirty cents across the table so he could buy himself another lettuce-and-tomato sandwich.

One thought to herself, 'Men are like icebergs; what appears on the surface is only one-tenth of what's underneath. It follows from this that Simon is ten times as wicked as he appears to be; how delightful, I can feel my knees turning to sawdust already.' Another thought to herself, 'It is usually on the third drink that they get down to the nitty-gritty. I will lure him to my apartment some evening, and pour two really stiff ones into him, and put Tchaikowski's *Pathetique* on the stereo, and then he will tell all, with tears streaming unchecked down his poor little face.'

Alas, Simon was always betrayed by his own high moral standards. As the various women who entered his life began to ask leading questions, he broke down and confessed that his lurid reputation was totally undeserved. 'Now, Simon,' they would reply, 'you must have some redeeming vices'; and at this he would tell them the terrible truth, that he was and always had been virtuous in word, thought and deed; following which they would scream with rage and disappointment and break the ketchup bottle over his head.

Simon Pure went back to see Novgorod, who frowned, saying, 'I expected something like that. Now we have only drastic measures left to us. I will place you in the hands of four female librarians – charter members of the Metropolitan Toronto Chain-Smoking, Home-Breaking and Martini-Swilling Association. Mix with them closely (which I fear you will not find difficult) and we'll see what happens.'

How Simon Pure fared after that has been stated for all time by the English poet William Blake: 'Vice is a monster of so frightful mien, as to be hated needs but to be seen; yet seen too oft, familiar with her face, we first endure, then pity, then embrace.' The librarians had no difficulty dragging Simon down to their own level. In scarcely more time than it takes to tell, he not only gave the appearance of wickedness, he actually was wicked all the way through; and this made him immensely popular with women.

Thus, through Novgorod's kindliness and wisdom, Simon Pure attained what he sought – wall-to-wall broads, and a different one of them out to dinner every night. His only troubles (we all have them, do we not?) are that he has been divorced three times, owes money all over town, has a serious drinking problem, and is under analysis.

A voice from the filing cabinet

Help, help! Au secours! Aiuto! I am a girl named Lynda Bird Hasenpfeffer, I've spent the last three years locked up in the filing cabinet of a wicked newspaper columnist, and now I want out. Hilf' mich! Socorro! Segitseg! Hjaelp! Pomoc! Pomagajtie!

I want to live! I'll accept any kind of existence he figures out for me, brief or crummy as it may be; the worst life imaginable is better than none at all. Besides, I don't like the kind of girls I've got in this file-folder with me; some of them are very low class. Screaming Mimi, there's one who always has a shower cap, a nightie and a toothbrush in her purse; Tawdry Audrey, there's one who always has a nightie and a toothbrush in her purse; Elizabeth Ardent, there's one who always has a toothbrush in her purse.

We're all in the same fix; he dreams us up, and then he stuffs us into the files, saying, 'I'll take you out in time for the North York futility rites,' and then he forgets about us. But we don't forget about him; we can't, he's the only hope we have of ever coming alive. Him! There he sits, cackling and snorting as he reads the letters from dish-illusioned mousewives in Hohum Hills; there's that washed-out secretary of his –

Luscious Lindy, he calls her, though to me she looks about as luscious as a wet cigar-butt; and there are all those smelly old bags of thirty-five and even forty who come hobbling in to waste his valuable time when they should be home knitting warm woolly sweaters for the Biafrans.

That Lindy creature, I'd like to tear out her blonde hair by its dark roots. She's disloyal to him; and he's too generous, too noble, too stupid to realize it. When his hearing aid is turned on, it's 'Yes, Richard' and 'No, Richard' and 'Can I get you a cup of coffee, Richard?' When he turns it off, she calls him Father Crime and the Prince of Whales and the Casanova of St. Petersburg. She never does any work that I can see; just sits there mooning over her pictures of Dustin Hoffman, Harry Belafonte, Arlo Guthrie and Rudolf Nureyev. I'd make a better secretary for him; I'm a highly accruate tpyist, and I can spell difficult words like paralell and acomodation and nesesary.

It wouldn't be easy, of course. He would call me some awful name like Minichest or Square Peg or the Witch of And-Or or Miss Potato Sack or the Venus de Mimico. But then he'd make up for it by bringing me flowers and taking me out to lunch at the Heretics Room or the Shock and Glee or Ed's Squarehouse. And then our hands would accidentally touch across the table, and he'd blush furiously and drop his cigarette into the onion soup. And then I'd go back to the office and tear up that horrible black book of his with all those addresses and phone numbers in it. Kill, kill!

But I don't insist on being his secretary; perhaps I could be the heroine in one of his stories. He'll do dreadful things to me, I know. He'll make me go out with men who put little wads of cotton batting in their ears; men who wear white socks with dark suits; men who say, 'If I was going to marry anybody, I'd marry you'; men who insist on telling me the real story behind President Kennedy's assassination; men whose mothers sit up waiting for them to come home.

He'll make me go out with men who furtively smoke cigarettes on the subway; men who wear beards which make them look and sometimes act like mountain goats; men who tell me all about British Israel; men who say, 'I'm going to educate you, baby' and 'I don't like my women wearing miniskirts' and 'No woman is going to tell me how to drive a car.' He'll make me go out with men who go out with men. But he'll let me win in the end. He usually lets women win in the end. That's what I like about him. That's what I hate about him.

But what's the use of daydreaming? First of all, I must attract his attention. Hmmm. Next time he opens the files, I'll cross my legs and give him a tantalizing glimpse of my black lace pantses, or I'll stand on tippy-toes and point my pointies at him; that should drive him mad with desire, and then I'll have him in my cruel power.

Of course, he may be too old to make that particular scene; they tell me it happens to most men around 35, and to newspapermen around 30, on account of their alcoholic excesses. In that case, I'll do my youth-and-innocence act. I'll turn my little face up to him like a flower, and I'll make my eyes round as saucers, and I'll let my lower lip tremble, saying, 'Oh sir, I'm so ignorant about life. I would like to sit at your feet and listen while you dispense your pearls of wisdom.'

That 'sir' bit really gets them. But – hey, what's happening? Someone's opening the file drawer! It's him, him, him, he heard me, he's going to let me out! No, it's Lindy. She's looking for that bottle of brandy she stashed away in the cabinet last night. Well, keep looking, you skinny bitch. I drank it. And when you go out to buy another, I hope you catch your heel in the subway grating and break your Modigliani neck.

Valley of the doldrums

ne of the most charming ceremonies around the *Mop and Pail* takes place at noon each day in the cafeteria. The editor, Dietrich Doppelganger, shakes a tin of saltpetre into the shepherd's pie, following which he gives a brief address requesting the staff to wear shoes, shave at least once a week, and refrain from inflating their expense accounts by more than 75 per cent. They applaud when it's over (simply because it's over), then wander off to attend the lurch of their choice.

I showed up for the occasion yesterday, and afterwards eavesdropped on a group of editorial writers chattering away to each other: 'You have to be firm with Doppelganger sometimes; he wouldn't let me do the editorial on Christian unity until I threatened to knock his teeth down his throat . . . I'm glad we're opposing American imperialism in Southeast Asia; if you ask me, they should court-martial that fellow Dewey . . . Doppelganger says he has a real treat for us policywise; we're coming out for mixed bathing, but of course only on weekdays . . . You mark my words, fellows, now that the Statute of Westminster has been passed, Canada will enjoy complete independence in her foreign policy . . . D.D. says that if I get my Grade 8, he'll let me do the ones on education.'

Doppelganger himself suddenly appeared before me, puffing away on one of the new strychnine filters. 'Novgorod! Where the hell have you been lately? We missed the hyena-like snarls and cackles proceeding from your office, the acrid aroma of burning papers, linoleum, desk-tops and elephant pants, the screams of rage when you referred to one of your numerous female visitors as Fanny Swill or Camel Chin or Grubby Mary or Lily of the Alley or the Grand Old Sag.'

I told him, 'While great progress is being made in all fields of medicine, few have seen more dramatic advances than that of ophthalmic surgery. In other words, I've been to the Toronto General Hospital for my annual sock in the eye.' Quentin Turgid frowned. 'I knew that. Did you get the bottle of brandy we sent you?' I answered, 'Oh yes. I drank most of it the night before my operation; by the time they rolled me into the O.R., I was anesthetized already. I suppose you want to know where I went after they threw me out of T.G.H. with a week's supply of fruit muffins, arrowroot biscuits and butterscotch blanc-mange. I flew to Winnipeg with three public-school students, four high-school students, and two adults; from Winnipeg, we all went on to Vancouver by bus.'

'That's a long haul,' said Gravy Brain. 'Didn't the kids get bored?' I assured him, 'Oh, no; they either slept or read comic books. While the adults admired the vast plains, the snow-capped peaks and the raging rivers, the kids sat engrossed in Dennis the Menace. I fear I annoyed them several times by drawing their attention away from Archie and

124

Jughead to some perilous glacier or some spectacular feat of railway engineering.'

'How did you manage for food?' asked the Wizard of Was. 'Oh that was easy. The kids sustained themselves with a simple but nourishing diet of hot dogs, potato chips, chocolate bars, French fries, soggy hamburgers, popsicles and Fanta. After being with the young at close quarters, I've decided they've an intake of 10,000 calories daily. But they burn it all up watching television, or standing in the line-up for *Planet of the Apes*.'

'Did you read the papers while you were away?' asked the Fog Prince. I shook my head. 'It's the same old stuff every day – someone got murdered, someone got elected, someone made a speech, someone went on strike.' Last Aid looked disapproving. 'That's no way for a newspaperman to talk. Stirring events have been taking place in Christiania, Constantinople and St. Petersburg, not to mention Hochelaga, Bytown, Fort Garry and Norway House. I was hoping you might change your negative attitude toward politics. We've an exciting situation in Canada today – a new Prime Minister who's a bachelor, only 48 years old, and eager for drastic reforms. You mark my words, the country will go a long way under Mackenzie King.'

As I turned to leave, Doom Service stuck out his hand in an impulsive gesture. 'Anyway, I'm glad to see you back, and perhaps your operation has been a blessing in disguise. An enforced vacation often has the effect of helping a writer – gives him some much-needed new ideas, straightens out his distorted perspective on things, makes him realize how he's been wasting his time and his talent. Now get in there, my boy, and sock it to 'em. Give the word to your gravid readers.' I took the hand and shook it, murmuring, 'Tankoos Yarmon.' He replied without hesitation. 'You're Welk.' Why does he always have to win?

I was a basic man in old T.O.

Does it surprise you (said the man at the bar) to find drinks being served here in Hell? They're actually part of the torment; you ask for brandy and get brimstone. As for the air conditioners you've seen around, they're part of the torment, too; they were installed by the same people who installed the escalators on the Toronto subway.

We're in a special section of Hell, did you know? It's reserved for men who were killed by women – by women they loved or, more frequently, by women who loved them. Come now, sir, don't profess surprise. A woman often kills the man she loves, that's the way she expresses her love, what you might call the last full measure of devotion.

Or again, she might kill the man who loves her. She is bored with being loved by him, let us say; or he has failed to send her his usual daily letter of adoration; or, while not wanting his love, she wants to make sure no other woman will ever get it; or she has bought a new dress and taken it home and has decided she doesn't like it.

My death took place last summer in Toronto, where for quite a few years I had played the role of being a basic man. You don't know what a basic man is? Good heavens above, let me tell you. The basic man has been well described in the sacred writings of one Rasputin J. Novgorod – who's expected, by the way, to be with us in person fairly soon. Novgorod has said, 'Every woman needs a man who loves her; it gives her a secure base from which to operate as she searches for a man to love.' Again, Novgorod has said, 'What every woman loves is to juggle several men at a time, while being absolutely certain of one of them.'

My role, sir, was to be that one man, the man who loved her, the man of whom she could feel certain as she plunged into varying degrees of romance with various other men – the man, in short, whom she could always come back to. I played this part with a woman named Polly Unsatiated, an English teacher at Woebegone C.I. As the basic man in her life, I was supposed to edit the love letters she wrote to other men, select little presents for her to send to other men, treat the scratches, bites and bruises given her by other men. As Novgorod has said in the sacred writings, 'A woman loves the man who tends her wounds almost as much as she loves the man who inflicts them on her.'

Polly would say to me, 'Oh, Frank, can you lend me $200? I am going to Montreal with an absolutely divine man and I do want to show him a good time. We'll be at the Chateau Cheesegrater, be sure to write every day and tell me you love me; a woman needs to feel secure in this wicked and ungrateful world. Oh, and by the way, phone Jim and Harry to tell them I am visiting my dear old mother in No Way, Man.'

Again, Polly would say to me, 'Frank, I have to be certain that you really love me. Is that truly the case?' When, as always, I answered yes, she would reply, 'That is great good news, and makes me the luckiest and happiest woman in the world. Now, Frank, I am in an awful jam. I promised Bill I would accompany him tonight to his immersion course in swimming, and I promised Joe I would accompany him to his crash course in driving, but what I really want to do is go with Bob to hear a new rock group called the Jarvis Street Approach. Will you tell Bill and Joe I've gone to Buenos Aires for a meeting of the Toronto Board of Education?'

Or again, she would say, 'Frank, I do not wish to exploit your love for me, or to use you in any way, that would be most unfair to you, but there is this utterly fascinating man I met at a cocktail party the other day, and I want to see him again. So I thought you might dream up some excuse for asking him out to lunch, and I would just accidentally wander into the restaurant, and you would spring up expressing joy and surprise and invite me to join you at your table. Oh, Frank, I just don't know how I would ever get along without you. Will you promise to love me until taxes are reduced, until the poverty problem is resolved, until the war ends in Vietnam?' And of course I would affectionately assent.

The time came when my sister-in-law showed up from Lower East Umbrage, N.S., and I took her out to tea and bought her some flowers and held her arm crossing the busy street. Unfortunately, this was noticed by Polly, who accused me of mendacity, infidelity and dereliction of duty, following which she fractured my occiput with her 75-pound handbag.

That's what brought me to Hell; and you, sir, what brought you here? I can clearly see the cause of your demise – all those nail files, letter-openers and hatpins sticking out of your back. Say, it just hit me! You must be Rasputin J. Novgorod, correct? So they finally got you, and I know what your punishment's going to be. Satan's doomed you to spend eternity playing poker and drinking beer with a bunch of the guys.